The
Ladies of Soissons

This very witty short novel is about an
imaginary community of English nuns who
left England for France with James II, went
through the French Revolution and the
First World War and got washed up in
Ireland, where they were completely bewildered, during the Second World War; it
ends with their return to France. The story
centres on the very varied characters of their
Mother Abbesses, some tremendous and
worldly, some timid, some heroic and
devout, but all human and credible.

The Ladies of Soissons

SIDNEY
CUNLIFFE-OWEN

Drawings by Pat Keely

THE NEWMAN PRESS

Westminster, Maryland

Printed in Great Britain
by Collins Clear-Type Press
London and Glasgow
for the Publishers
THE NEWMAN PRESS
Westminster, Maryland

To Sister Ratcliffe

I was lying one day last spring in bed No. 12 of Hull Martin Ward of the West London Hospital, feeling, and doubtless looking, very 'gormless', when you hurried past and called back over your shoulder rather crossly, 'Why don't you do some writing?'

The result is this book which was written entirely in bed No. 12 while under your care. Therefore it is only fitting that I should dedicate this book to you, which I do with the greatest pleasure.

I

THE YOUNG Abbess Eileen sat on her favourite rock on the lakeside skipping flat pebbles over the water till the agonised screams of the Americans reminded her that she was disturbing the fish.

'Am I charging them enough?' she wondered. 'Surely the good God does not mind one overcharging Americans, for surely heaven is a quiet place and He does not like noise.' The Americans were, she reflected, the chief source of the convent's livelihood, with its twin lakes so splendidly stocked with fish. Moreover, the secular proprietors of fishing rights in Connemara and Mayo charged much more. Then there was the bathing in the hydrangea- and fuchsia-ringed bay where the heaving waters of the Atlantic, straight from their own country, came in quietly among the rocks. And the arboretum, the finest in Ireland.

She thought, not for the first time, what an anachronism I am in the second half of the twentieth century, a Mitred Abbess. True there was one in England at Stanbrook, the famous Abbess Scholastica, the friend of Bernard Shaw, and there were several in the Rhineland, who even now kept up considerable state and had the roads cleared, the troops out, and flags flying when they passed through the towns in procession on their patronal feast days. And there were some in Italy and some in Austria. But she was the only one in Ireland, the only one of Irish nationality (though they still belonged to the French Congregation), and the youngest in the world.

She had been elected in 1956 at the age of 29, by the wish of the formidable Abbess Catherine, the 'Great Abbess', who had reigned for fifty years and then abdicated in favour of her beloved protégée, Madame Eileen. Of course the elections of Abbesses, for life, are by secret ballot, and so it was in this case, but the nuns were all so frightened of Madame Catherine that they would not have dared go against her wishes. Even now, after being four years Abbess, Eileen still could not believe that she, the uneducated girl from the last of the claddaghs in Mayo, should have risen to such heights so quickly. When she thought of her predecessors, refined great ladies of France, wondrously learned, she sometimes felt quite scared, but she had, in fact, a great deal of determination underlying a quiet, almost timid, manner. She had many reforms in mind. The 'Great Abbess' Catherine had raised the Community to heights it had never reached before, especially during the 1914—18 and the recent wars, but after fifty

years of rule and at eighty years of age, her hold had
inevitably relaxed.

And then the French members of the Community
would not pull their weight. Evacuated from
Soissons as long ago as 1940, they still wanted to go
back, as the old Abbess had in fact done. They hated
Ireland, *pays sauvage et brute où il pleut même plus qu'en
Angleterre!* They held the Church in Ireland to be
practically in schism, because the hierarchy seldom
took any notice of Papal Bulls, and because they
were always referring to *les temps avant St Patrice*,
when they were independent of Rome and made
Saints, thousands of them, Brigits and Brendans and
Gobnaits, without any right to do so whatsoever,
and none of them are in the Roman Missal.

So the young Abbess determined to get rid of the
French nuns by degrees and replace them with Irish
girls, and herself to cease to be Madame de Soissons,
and to become instead the Lady Abbess of Lingmoor.

And yet she was the latest of a proud line. She
passed in review in her mind's eye the portraits in
the great hall, starting with the Abbess Anne, and
ending with her humble self, the twelve Abbesses,
each with their mitre, cope and crosier, the same
which she would find placed beside her stall when
she went indoors for Compline that evening. Some
great, some small, they all looked most regal except
herself, and she looked, she thought, like a young

girl dressed up for a masquerade. She must acquire dignity. With her fair hair (invisible of course), china-blue eyes, pink and white skin and retroussé nose, this most un-Irish-looking Irish Abbess was exceedingly pretty, but as she never looked at herself in a mirror, she was only half aware of the fact. Men enjoyed kneeling and kissing her ring; women were not so keen. It savoured of Pope Joan and all that to kneel to a woman prelate. The young Abbess had no desire to be a Pope Joan, but she did want, and fully intend, beneath that deceptive mildness, to become one of the great Abbesses. Suddenly it flashed across her mind, for no particular reason, that one of her reforms must be fire drill, a minor one and she soon forgot about it.

She got up to walk back to the Abbey. 'Say, Abbess, this sure is good,' cried one of the Americans catching up with her and displaying four large trout. 'I'm very glad to hear it,' she answered, trying to maintain her dignity. How annoying to be so young, she kept thinking.

How well she remembered each word spoken on that memorable day when she had the first intimation that she would be made an Abbess! Madame Catherine had sent for her. She was acting novice mistress at the time.

'*Viens ici, petite. Je vais abdiquer.*'

'Abdicate, Madame . . . but why? I can't imagine . . . and are you allowed to by the Rule?'

'*Je ne sais pas*. I have written to the Abbess-General in Rome, but whatever she answers, I shall go. I am tired, and want to spend my last few days in France away from this *pays barbare*, and I shall suggest . . . of course I can do no more than that . . . I shall *hint*, that you are elected my successor.'

'Me, Madame? Me? Never! Oh never!'

'You would make a fine Abbess.'

'Impossible.'

'Nothing is impossible with God's help. Pray to Him.'

'But me in your place . . . a young girl . . . it is unthinkable!'

'Perhaps they will not elect you.'

'Oh, I hope not . . . I pray not. I could not bear so great a responsibility.'

But Madame Eileen *was* elected. Madame Catherine watched over her for a couple of months afterwards, and then announced her departure, for France, where she was going to live with a Community on the outskirts of Paris.

'You're all right,' she said abruptly one morning to the young Abbess. 'You'll do. You're in the saddle now. You will come and see me off.'

So together they drove to Galway, along the islanded shores of Lough Corrib, and sat for four hours in a first-class carriage gazing out over the weeping hills and dreary bogs.

'*Allons au wagon restaurant* . . . cheer ourselves up
with a cup of tea,' said Madame Catherine, and
when they were seated . . . '*Dieu! que je suis contente de
quitter ce pays affreux, cette religion schismatique, ces
mornes collines, cette pluie perpétuelle, ce manque d'intelligence et de savoir-faire.*'

A gentleman sitting opposite looked most startled
and answered the Abbess in perfect French, defending the Irish Church as the most loyal in Europe, the
highbrows of Dublin as the most sophisticated after
the Parisians, the Irish culture as one of the oldest in
the world, and what about Yeats and Shaw, A.E.,
Lady Gregory, Synge, Orpen, Jack Yeats, and so
on.

The Abbess had never heard of any of them and
would not have approved of them if she had, but
against such a spate of erudition she was powerless.
She got up and went grumbling back to her com-
partment.

'You've been kissing the Blarney Stone,' the
young Abbess threw at him over her shoulder as she
left the restaurant car.

'You're Irish at any rate. I can tell by your voice,'
he said. 'Put the old girl in her place for me, will
you?'

The young Abbess's blood ran cold at the thought
of the explosion which would have occurred had
Madame Catherine been aware that she had been
referred to as *vieille fille*, but she was back in her seat

gazing mournfully out of the window with her Office Book lying open on her lap.

'*Ah, que je suis contente de retourner en France après ces longues années d'exil!*' she exclaimed as the Liverpool packet came in sight, moored to its anchorage at North Wall. 'Don't you wish you were coming with me to *la belle et douce France?*' she cried as they got down from the taxi and felt the tang of the sea air mingled with the stink of the Liffey invade their nostrils. '*Mais non,*' she answered her own question. '*Au contraire.* You are Irish and you love your native land. It is quite natural and quite right to love *son pays,* to love *la patrie.* But how you can, I really cannot comprehend,' she went on, 'and you so intelligent . . . to be content with those bogs . . . I fear that when I am safely out of the way you will turn the Community into an Irish house, despite its centuries-old connection with my country. *Eh bien, tant pis* . . . I shall not be there to see.'

'And I love Lingmoor, Madame.'

'I know you do. One can see that. And I am pleased. You will prosper there, because of that. I am sure of it.'

In the cabin on the boat, Madame Catherine suddenly knelt at the feet of the young Abbess and asked her blessing. Madame Eileen was completely overcome, and fell on her knees also. 'No, no! Bless me, my mother!' she exclaimed.

The old lady burst out laughing and scrambled to

her feet. 'What a spectacle we are . . . two women grovelling to each other and quarrelling as to who should bless whom! *Debout, mon enfant*, and let me give you a farewell kiss.'

She embraced the young Abbess tenderly with tears in her eyes, and then exclaimed, 'Now go . . . go!' and opening the cabin door almost pushed Madame Eileen out.

The young Abbess, her eyes blurred with her tears, stumbled down the gangway and stood on the windswept quay, where the fumes of Guinness were being borne down river on the off-shore wind, among the swirling débris of departure, bits of paper eddying in the air currents, orange peel upon the water, paper bags and greedy seagulls screaming, until the ship startled her with its hooting and soon afterwards floated silently away down the river towards the open sea.

The young Abbess hoped that Madame Catherine would appear on deck and wave good-bye, but she could not see her, and turned away disconsolately to find a taxi that would take her to the convent where she was to spend the night. She felt more lonely than she had ever done before in her life.

2

In the year 1688 there was a small Community of Benedictine nuns living at Brentford in Middlesex, under the protection of the Queen Dowager, Catherine of Braganza. The thought of continuing to live under the rule of the usurper, Dutch William, who had just landed at Torbay, was abhorrent to them. The ascendency of the Protestant religion was now inevitable.

So the Prioress and all her forty nuns packed their bags and, hiring two carts, had themselves conveyed to Tilbury, where the lawful King James II was embarking for Ireland.

They stood on the quay, the wind blowing their veils askew, and begged to be taken on board. The master of the transport lying astern of the royal yacht, hearing their cries and lamentations, came on deck and, on being told by the Prioress what they wanted, declared that it was quite out of the question to take forty ladies aboard his ship, and that this was a military expedition and that no women were allowed.

Hearing the commotion King James came out of

his cabin on to the deck of the royal yacht, and, on being told the cause, said, 'The prayers of the religious are worth an army corps to me; let them come.'

So the nuns were embarked, both the captain and the troops who had to give up their quarters and sleep in odd corners between decks, grumbling greatly, and that night the flotilla sailed down the Thames on the falling tide and four days later reached Ireland.

Throughout the campaign which ended in the Battle of the Boyne, the nuns were most useful to King James. They were probably the first hospital nurses, for they worked in the front line, tending the wounded, tearing up their habits for tourniquets, giving cups of water, comforting. Two of them were killed by cannon shot.

After the Battle of the Boyne, they fled with James to France. There the King became a pensioner of Louis XIV, who was anxious to seize any opportunity of annoying Dutch William, and asked the French King if he could do something for his poor faithful nuns who had fought with him so gallantly, and given up all to follow him, and who, not understanding one word of the language, were now uncomfortably and precariously lodged with some Benedictines in Paris who wished to be rid of them as soon as possible.

Some time later Louis let James know that he

could not do much for the Community, but that
there was, at Soissons, a disused convent, from
which, for laxity, the Archbishop of Rheims had
evicted the nuns and dispersed them among other
houses, and that the Englishwomen could go there.
It would be at least a roof over their heads, and their
own roof, and if they could find ways and means of
restoring the property and making themselves comfortable, perhaps by giving English lessons, or taking paying guests, why so much the better. Meanwhile he would give them a small sum of money to
start them off, from his own privy purse.

The nuns were exceedingly grateful and made
known that they would pray for King Louis XIV
every day of their lives (which they are still doing in
this year of grace 1960). They migrated to Soissons
and for the first time saw the place which was to be
their home until the year 1940.

It was a huge old rambling place behind high
walls, centred round a chapel, the classical interior of
which struck the nuns as exceedingly modern. 'Just
like Sir Christopher Wren,' they declared. There was
a pleasant cloister, the cells were large and airy, more
like rooms, there were the remains of a large vegetable and a small flower garden, but everything was
in a state of disrepair, roofs gaping, windows broken,
shutters banging in the breeze.

The nuns set to work. They quickly made friends
with the local carpenters and masons, who admired

their courage and determination, and for whom their exploits on the battlefield and in voyaging so far across the sea were almost legendary. 'None of our French religious would dare so much,' they declared. That nuns should leave the shelter of their convents to fight and travel for the sake of their King and their Faith caused in them the deepest admiration, and they helped all they could to restore the property and make it habitable.

In a couple of years' time, the nuns had restored the vegetable garden and had cows in the meadow, and gathered fruit from the orchard, so were practically self-supporting as regards food; the chapel had been reconsecrated by the Archbishop of Rheims himself; English lessons were being given to the sons and daughters of the local nobility, for English was becoming a fashionable language to learn, owing to the reputation of the philosophers, Newton and Locke; and finally the nuns had set aside a suite of rooms (for the convent had been built to house a much larger Community than their own) for elderly ladies, dowagers of good family. Here they could be looked after, waited on, and could receive their friends, and go out and come in as they wished . . . and were charged a monthly fee fully commensurate with these privileges. The nuns themselves had started to learn French, and as it seemed unlikely that they would be able to return to England in the foreseeable future, the Prioress welcomed applications from French girls to enter the novitiate, and decided that eventually the Community must become totally French. This would obviate the pangs of exile and also enable the Community to become affiliated to the French Benedictines, with the corresponding advantages. At present they still belonged to the English Congregation, which was highly inconvenient.

It was in the year 1710 that King Louis XIV came to the neighbourhood of Soissons for the last time. Much of his long reign and all of his money had been spent campaigning on this north-east frontier and precious little had he got out of it. On this occasion Madame de Maintenon was with him. She came as far as Soissons where she left him to go and spend a few days with her old friend, the Marquise de Briquiers, who had a suite of rooms in the convent. The King came to pick her up on his way back to Versailles, after a so-called triumphal tour of his north-eastern provinces. By this time he was becoming most agitated over the state of his soul. He could not hope to live much longer, for he was already over 70. For years past, Bossuet in public from the pulpit, and Madame de Maintenon in private, had been urging him to consider his latter end. His life had been far from exemplary, and, according to Bossuet, if he did not obtain powerful intercession from some professional source quickly, his future condition in the next world would be less comfortable than it had been in this one. So he asked the nuns to redouble their prayers on his behalf, and raised the Priory to the status of an Abbey, as a reward for so doing. Two years later, in 1712, more frightened than ever, he asked for more prayers and Masses in perpetuity, and raised the Abbess to the status of a Mitred Abbess, having the privileges, but not the powers, of a Prince-Bishop, like those of Trier, Mainz and Speyer. At the time of the Revocation of the Edict of Nantes, which had driven so much valuable trade out of France, Louis had exempted a group of weavers living in La Rochelle, because, though Huguenots, they wove better than anyone else in France. It was they who were commissioned to make the newly-appointed Abbess's cope and mitre, while her crosier, silver and elaborately chased, was made by the best silversmith in Paris. The cope was especially magnificent, portraying the Holy Trinity up aloft, with a cloud of Mitred Abbesses rising up to meet It, sponsored by a satisfied-looking St Benedict on the one side and St Peter on the other. The lower part of the cope was embroidered with flowers, and round the bottom ran a frieze of St Benedict's ravens from Subiaco. There were masses of thick gold thread and the present Abbess finds it so heavy to wear that she has had shoulder pads made to wear beneath her habit to prevent her skin being chafed.

Henceforth the Abbess would be known as

Madame de Soissons, her fully-professed nuns as Les Dames de Soissons, and her novices and postulants as Les Sœurs de Soissons. It was the first Mitred Abbess, Anne, who had made the coach drawn by six white horses, which someone who has seen both declared to be as lovely as the Queen of Britain's Coronation coach, though for Neptune and the trident it has angels and archangels. The Abbesses used it until 1940, when Field-Marshal Goering looted it and took it to his East Prussian estate of Karinhall. This was looted by the Russians, who took the coach to Moscow, where it may be seen in the Kremlin Museum, complete with six prancing and caparisoned white horses and a notice pointing out the laxity, wealth and luxury of the Roman Church.

Thus the Ladies of Soissons started on their magnificent, but scarcely edifying, career, which was to be abruptly changed by the French Revolution.

3

THE EIGHTEENTH century was a period in the life of
the Community which was usually glossed over by
the young Abbess on the occasions when she had to
show distinguished visitors over the Abbey and
passed in review the portrait gallery of Abbesses.

This was strange in a way because, although the
Community had not been noted for piety during that
period, it had been the wealthiest and grandest community of its kind in France and the splendours of
the Ladies of Soissons were known from one end of
the kingdom to the other.

All this came to an abrupt end with the outbreak
of the French Revolution. The Abbess at the time
was the Abbess Clare, who had been elected in 1772,
seventeen years before the Revolution broke out.

She had not paid much attention to stories of
trouble which had come to her ears. Soissons seemed
very quiet and staid and conservative as always.
When she heard that the King and Queen had been
forced to return to Paris, she thought it was a good
idea and understood that they were treated with

every honour and consideration and lived in the Tuileries Palace.

When, therefore, she received one morning a message from Madame de Compiègne, the Carmelite Abbess, asking if she could be so kind as to come and visit her to discuss an important matter, she did not suspect for a moment what that important matter could be. Madame de Compiègne explained that she could not come to Soissons because she and her Community were strictly enclosed, but that she understood that Madame de Soissons possessed every facility for making a comfortable journey to her.

This somewhat feline allusion to the coach and six white horses rather nettled Madame de Soissons. However, she sent a message back to say that she would come in two days' time. She had never met Madame de Compiègne, who was not a Benedictine, and could not imagine why the latter should want to see her.

It was a beautiful spring morning when she set off two days later. She took with her her secretary, Dame Thérèse. In the spacious coach the dining-table had been set up and there was a picnic basket full of cold meats, cheese, fruit, bread and wine, and Madame Clare said they would picnic somewhere in the forest under the trees.

Their way led right across the forest of Compiègne. The track was a broad grass ride, soft beneath the springless coach and silent beneath the wooden wheels.

The Abbess lay back contentedly among her cushions. 'This really is delectable,' she exclaimed to her companion. 'How good God is to create such beauty and to give us the senses wherewith to appreciate it. I can't think why Madame de Compiègne wishes to see me, but I am glad she does, as it has given an excuse for a delightful outing.'

The trees stretched endlessly on both sides of the track. The Abbess let down the window and the fresh damp air blew into the stuffy coach. She could now hear the birds singing, and they saw deer, and a fox, and a weasel. At midday the Abbess ordered the coachman to stop, and said she would lunch alfresco under the trees. With the help of the postilions, the table was brought out from the coach and the picnic set up with the Abbess's second-best set of silver to eat it with. The wine was removed from the icebox at the back of the coach, and uncorked. A rug and cushions were placed upon the grass up against the trunk of a large beech tree, and the Abbess and Madame Thérèse settled down to a good tuck-in and siesta after.

Towards sunset they reached Compiègne. The Carmelite Abbess was on the steps to welcome them. She was an alarming woman with black beetling eyebrows, black eyes like gimlets, and a moustache. She cast disapproving looks at the great golden coach with the six white horses, the three postilions, and the coachman and footman on the box.

Madame de Soissons descended with stately dignity and advancing towards her colleague, embraced her perfunctorily.

'What are we to do about your men?' asked Madame de Compiègne. 'We are an enclosed house as you know and can admit no males.'

'Have you no sheds, no outbuildings, Madame? In any case the horses must be stabled and fed.'

Madame de Compiègne thought awhile, then sighed.

'Maybe we could . . .' she began. 'Yes, perhaps that would serve. Could your secretary perhaps accompany your coachman and one of my girls to see where . . . so that you will know . . .'

After this somewhat vague speech, and the arrival of the girl, who turned out to be an old nun of about eighty, Madame de Compiègne led the way indoors, and presented her guest in the parlour with 'a little collation'.

'Little it is,' thought Madame Clare who was hungry after her long drive. A plate of cheese, some bread, and a glass of water. She looked at her surroundings. They were equally austere. Austerest of all was her hostess. Madame Clare inwardly gave thanks to God that He had not given her any desire to be a Carmelite.

After a few desultory remarks, while Madame

Clare ate up the bread and cheese, Madame de Compiègne came to the point.

'They have guillotined the King,' she said.

Madame Clare was speechless with horror.

'*Ils ont fait quoi!*' she cried, unbelievingly.

'They have killed the King,' repeated Madame de Compiègne. 'Now,' she continued after a pause, 'the Revolution really starts! Robespierre has set up Committees of Public Safety all over the country. There is one here in Compiègne, and I daresay you will find there is one in Soissons. Their principal object is to destroy religion, for they have set up a Goddess of Reason, a Parisian harlot having been chosen to play the part, in the Place Louis XIV in Paris.'

'*Quelle horreur!*' exclaimed the terrified Madame Clare, her eyes starting out of her head like the eyes of a prawn.

'So you see what we must do,' continued Madame de Compiègne.

'Yes, indeed. We must . . .' It was on the tip of Madame Clare's tongue to say 'flee the country . . . skip over the border into the Netherlands or Germany,' but she pulled herself up in time, realising from the fanatical look of those burning black eyes upon her, that Madame de Compiègne was about to suggest a very different solution.

'We must go to Paris,' the implacable voice continued, 'and shed our blood for Christ upon the guillotine. What joy, what a privilege is ours to win

28

the crown of martyrdom! I have asked my girls and one and all they welcome the golden crown.'

As indeed they did, and three months later Madame de Compiègne and her Community went to the guillotine in Paris and Poulenc wrote an opera about them, *Les Carmélites*, which was produced at Covent Garden in 1958.

Madame Clare reflected that if she were to ask her 'girls', the answer would be very different . . .'over the frontier and as quickly as possible', a verdict in which she herself heartily concurred.

She was beginning to feel very frightened. What if the members of the Committee of Public Safety, which already existed in Compiègne according to her hostess, should have seen her arrive. The coach and six white horses were not exactly inconspicuous. She wished she had not promised to stay the night, though the horses must be rested. But she would have preferred to camp out in the forest, sleeping in the coach, had she known. What if the revolutionaries came to fetch her in the middle of the night and carted her off to Paris to the guillotine, accompanied probably by this horrid woman sitting opposite her, probing her with her eyes, which would make it even worse. No, decidedly, she was not ready for martyrdom.

All that night she lay in terror on her hard pallet bed, unable to sleep. Madame Thérèse, also quaking with fear, lay near her. Each time the night watchman's step was heard outside the window, the Abbess shuddered. 'It is them,' she would whisper. '*Ah non, ne dites pas ça,*' came the reply.

By four in the morning, the Abbess had had enough. It was beginning to get light. The birds were singing. 'Go and find Paul,' she told Madame Thérèse, 'and tell him to harness the horses immediately. Tell him it is essential we return to Soissons as soon as possible.'

Dame Thérèse found Paul, the head coachman, sleeping in some straw in a kind of woodshed, surrounded by heavily snoring postilions. The dawn was so beautifully soft and clear that she found it hard to imagine revolution and bloodshed stalking the land. She woke up Paul. At first he was angry, almost rude, staggered to his feet grumbling that the horses had not had enough rest and nor had he, but when Dame Thérèse told him the reason, he changed completely. Kicking the postilions he bellowed, 'Up, up, all of you, and harness quickly. The Revolution has come to Compiègne. They are after us!'

Half an hour later the coach rumbled up to the front door of the convent. Madame de Soissons hoped to slip out unobserved, but Madame de Compiègne, straight-backed, black-browed and inflexible, was standing on the steps as Madame de Soissons half turned to get into the coach.

'Why so early, Madame?' came the harsh voice.

'Without hearing Mass, without taking breakfast?'

'I must get back to my nuns,' panted Madame Clare, 'and warn them. They may be in great danger.'

'I am sure they will know how to behave at such a time,' replied Madame de Compiègne calmly. 'I take it ill that you should wish to leave me so soon. I wished to present to you my girls and show you the convent. We possess interesting relics of martyrs from earlier persecutions.'

Madame Clare had no wish to be added to the list, her thigh-bone in a dusty glass case, her little finger up on a shelf in the sacristy. She wished to be buried whole and complete, when her time came, in a cemetery, and die an ordinary penitent sinner like everyone else. They could keep their haloes. Moreover, she asked herself, what was the point of meeting 'girls' whom she would never see again, and being shown over a convent shortly to be handed over to the local Goddess of Reason?

'You are kind, Madame,' she declared, looking at the odious woman, 'but I have food in the coach, and as to Mass, in an emergency such as this, it is a pleasure that must be forgone.'

Whereat, before Madame de Compiègne could argue any further, she sprang into the coach and shut the door crying, '*En avant, Paul, et à toute allure. Il est déjà tard!*'

It was in fact only twenty to five, but Paul drove

31

through the town as if possessed, the postilions cracking their whips and whacking their horses. At one point the great cumbrous coach nearly upset as they took a sharp corner on one of the narrow cobbled streets. The noise was terrific, like a first-class thunderstorm. Citizens, including the members of the Committee of Public Safety, put their heads under the bedclothes and prayed. Ten minutes later the refugees were in the forest.

It looked more beautiful, more cool, delightful, Arcadian, than ever. 'Like one of Monsieur Watteau's pictures,' said Dame Thérèse, but Madame Clare saw Robespierre lurking behind every tree and would not allow the coach to stop till Paul finally brought it to a halt, climbed down from the box and told Madame Clare that if the horses were not rested they would drop down dead and so would he.

'You must not do that,' said Madame Clare, 'for tonight we must continue to the German frontier.'

'Tonight?' Paul was aghast.

'Or else we shall be murdered in our beds,' declared the Abbess prophetically.

'Did she tell you that? Her with the moustache . . . back there.' He gestured in the direction of Compiègne.

'She did and worse. We have not a moment to lose.'

'*Sapristi! Nom d'un chien!* But it is impossible. We shall never get there. Are all the ladies going?'

'Yes, indeed.'

'Because the horses for their carriages will be fresh, so I think it would be best for you and Madame Thérèse to go in one of those, and leave these behind. Also it is less conspicuous.'

The Abbess saw the force of the last remark, but could not bear the thought of leaving her coach and six white horses behind and appearing at Aachen drawn by only two black ones and no postilions . . . She had already rehearsed her entry. She would send a postilion or groom on ahead to inform the authorities that the great Abbess, Madame de Soissons no less, was a fugitive from her own country where she had escaped the guillotine by minutes, and that she threw herself at the feet, metaphorically, of a generous people, and by that she hoped to find the Cardinal Archbishop in person waiting at the city gates, and thereafter to be suitably housed and fed till the Revolution was over.

'*Les révolutions ne durent pas,*' she told Madame Thérèse sagely. '*Après elles, la tyrannie, mais la tyrannie des grands et le respect pour la religion. C'est toujours la démocratie qu'il faut étouffer. Elle est l'ennemi perpétuel.*'

From which it will be seen that the Abbess, though not heroic, was no fool.

They stopped for half an hour and ate bread and drank wine sitting, as before, upon the grass, but the shadow of Robespierre and Danton and the

King's death and the tall black shape of the guillotine, were like hostile soldiers stalking them from tree to tree, edging ever nearer, and there was a blight upon the blue sky. The Abbess kept looking at her watch uneasily. She had promised Paul *une bonne demi-heure* for she did not wish the horses to break down. Besides she knew Paul would not stir till it pleased him. She depended absolutely on him for many things and he knew himself to be an indispensable part of the convent's equipment.

He had finished eating, was sound asleep and snoring loudly, his ugly red face turned up towards the sun. The horses, hobbled, were cropping the grass. The *bonne demi-heure* became two hours, for the Abbess, who had lain awake all night quaking, fell asleep, and so did Dame Thérèse.

At last someone woke up and there was a fearful commotion as the horses were fetched, harnessed, while the grooms and postilions rubbed their eyes and swore. It was at least another *bonne demi-heure* before the coach got moving, and it was dark before it at last emerged from the forest on to the Soissons road.

Tired though she was the Abbess immediately assembled her nuns and gave them the alternatives, martyrdom or flight. At first they thought they were expected to voice their wish for immolation, and stood silent with hangdog, embarrassed expressions. But when the Abbess said, 'I know which I shall choose,' and jerked her head in the direction of the frontier, they came to life and heartily agreed to the last woman.

The Abbess bade them pack up the valuables, the silver and gold chalices and monstrances from the sacristy, her own cope, mitre and crosier, the tabernacles . . . Monsieur Perouge, their chaplain, was coming with them . . . she had sent him a message . . . and he would safeguard the Hosts. They would hear Mass and receive Communion before they left which was to be at two in the morning. The pensionnaires must fend for themselves. They all had enough money to take them over the frontier if they wished to go. All the silver and gold-plated knives and forks, finger-bowls and cups and goblets, must be taken. All these things were to be distributed among the occupants of the twenty carriages, and some she would take with her in the coach. They would leave by different roads through the town, so as to be less conspicuous and noisy, and would rendezvous at the Rheims cross-roads eight miles outside the town. The Abbess that night exercised generalship worthy of Napoleon, whom later she was so much to admire. Her dispositions made, she retired to the chapel to pray. She remained there till Father Perouge arrived to say Mass. She saw her nuns off carriage by carriage, many weeping, all terrified. When the last had gone she herself, Dame Thérèse and Father Perouge got into the great

golden coach, the weary white horses staggered and
yawned as they gave the initial pull against the huge
inertia of the great vehicle, and so the Abbess left
Soissons.

Ten hours later they crossed the frontier at
Aachen. The Abbess had sent her groom ahead, and
sure enough there was the Cardinal Archbishop and
his clergy at the city gate, waiting, together with a
vast crowd of people who cheered and knelt and
prayed, and the delighted Abbess found that the
'Summer Schloss' of the Prince Cardinal Archbishop had been put at her disposal for the duration.
She was glad she had kept the coach. It was worthy
of its new home.

4

FOR FOUR years the Community remained at Aachen, where they led much the same life that they had led at Soissons. They gave French lessons to the sons and daughters of the nobility, for French was now as fashionable as English had been a century ago, owing to the philosophy of J. J. Rousseau especially and its popularity, so that every well-bred man and woman must be able to quote Rousseau in the original. They also took pensionnaires, and were favoured by the acquaintance of many people of importance in the city, who were delighted to receive the Abbess and her nuns in their houses.

Eventually, however, Bonaparte became First Consul and the Revolution was over and the tyranny, which the Abbess had predicted, began. Bonaparte would have nothing to do with atheism, despite his avowed intention of upholding the principles of the Revolution, and the fact that he commanded revolutionary armies. 'Of course there is a God,' he declared. 'Every soldier knows that. I intend to uphold the Catholic religion in which I was

born and in which I shall die, because it supports
Law and Order.'

The Abbess thoroughly approved of this senti-
ment and the female upholders of Law and Order
prepared to quit the 'Summer Schloss' and return to
uphold Law and Order in Soissons.

They had a great farewell, including a party with
fireworks, and were escorted to the city gate by a
throng of people all anxious to receive the Abbess's
blessing. Madame Clare sat regally in the golden
coach, bowing, smiling, and distributing largesse
and blessings impartially out of the window; the six
white horses broke into a gallop, the postilions singing and cracking their whips, and so they galloped
into France again, the twenty carriages containing
the nuns, each with its two black horses, trailing
out behind far along the road like the tail of a comet.

The excitement and enthusiasm in Soissons knew
no bounds. Well outside the city limits the crowds
had already gathered and when the Abbess's coach
appeared in view there were cries and cheers and
sobs. '*Elles sont rentrées! Enfin elles sont là!*'

In the Place opposite the cathedral, all the clergy
and the Bishop were lined up to welcome the Abbess
formally. Bands played, troops lined the streets,
dense crowds waved and cheered and fought with
each other for a better view. The Abbess descended
from the coach and entered the cathedral for a short
service of thanksgiving. On leaving to the sound of

pealing bells she did not enter the coach, but appeared vested in cope and mitre, and carrying the crosier. In front of her went the crucifix, then the secular and regular clergy, followed by the Bishop, all singing the Te Deum, then two little girls strewing rose petals at the Abbess's feet, then an acolyte carrying an aspersorium, and finally Madame Clare, handsome, majestic, dignified, followed by all her nuns, asperging busily with her left hand and blessing with her right.

Thus they came home, accompanied by a storm of cheering and not a dry eye in the place. The convent was untouched, though unkempt, everything dirty and dusty, the paths in the garden unweeded, the flowers run riot, the chapel cold and empty. But an army of willing helpers came to aid the nuns and in two or three weeks' time, the Abbess was able to send out invitations for her homecoming feast.

Meanwhile she had been touched by the number of letters and personal messages she had received. 'Soissons was drab and bleak without you all!' 'We missed the happy faces of the religious in our streets.' 'We missed your visits, honouring us in our own homes.' 'The presence of the Ladies of Soissons gives the town a peculiar cachet such as no other town in France possesses.'

At the feast the Abbess was at her very best. She was now, in middle age, an exceedingly handsome woman, with great dignity, poise, and presence. She had a charming smile, she moved beautifully, her voice was full, rich and melodious, and she chose her words with care and spoke her subtle language with extreme elegance and attention to all its nuances. Worldly and not very pious she might be, but her religion, so far as it went, was utterly sincere, and she was admirably fitted to be the head of a Benedictine house at the end of the eighteenth century.

On this night, as she watched the feasting, and saw the happy faces of her nuns chatting away to their friends from the town and to the returned pensionnaires, and doubtless recalling their many adventures in Aachen, trivial incidents they would be for us, but full of thrills for them, the Abbess suddenly felt the tears come into her eyes and went outside into the garden for a moment to be alone. There was a moon, and the night was very still. She could hear the horses in the stable munching their hay. Suddenly there came upon her, as it comes to all of us, however sinful, at least once in our lives, lasting for perhaps a second but never forgotten, and vouchsafed continuously only to the Saints, a mystical awareness of the glory of God. For a brief space the Abbess saw things as they are, glorified by the hand of their creator. The moon, the rose bushes, the trees, the grass in the meadow, all became Real. She saw them for an instant as God sees them, not as we see them through the medium of our bodily senses, but spiritually. In the same way she heard the horses munching and the distant laughter of the guests, and she knew then that all things worked for good, and that events such as the French Revolution were of the devil and the fruit of original sin, but the glory of God was the supreme fact of the universe, and even as she realised it the vision died away, and she returned to her guests, gracious and smiling, a great lady indeed, but a mystic no more.

But for a period of two seconds she had been. She had been one with St Teresa of Avila and St John of the Cross, with St Francis, St Thomas à Kempis and St Catherine of Siena. The Abbess Clare went to bed that night justified.

5

UNDER NAPOLEON's rule they prospered exceedingly. The Empress Josephine spent a night with
them; they were very grand. But the climax came a
year or two before the death of Abbess Clare when
the young second Empress, Marie-Louise of Austria,
lodged with the Community the night before meeting her husband, to whom she had been married by
proxy, at the Palace of Compiègne. This was something ! Josephine, amiable and good though she was
in her latter days, was nevertheless only a Creole
from the West Indian island of Martinique, but
Marie-Louise was the niece of Marie Antoinette and
the granddaughter of the Empress Maria Teresia,
and she behaved accordingly (largely from shyness
and fright), being as *hautaine*, silent and disdainful,
as the most snobbish of nuns could wish.

She, a young girl who had never left Austria, was
scared of this country with which her father had
recently been at war, scared of her husband, this
bumptious little Italian general whom she had never
seen, who was reputed to tweak people's ears in
public as a sign of endearment. Napoleon on his side

was also scared at the thought of having to make
love to an imperious daughter of the Hapsburgs.
The Abbess accompanied the frightened girl to
Compiègne at the latter's request, and there she was
able to see the dream of her latter days in the flesh,
the Emperor Napoleon. She thought him far better-
looking than she had ever imagined. He was short,
but he had palely romantic classical features, beautiful hands and feet, and he had not yet grown stout.
She curtsied to the ground before him, and then
stood up, a splendid, majestic figure in her old age.
Her repressed motherly instincts would have liked
to take this poor scared little Emperor in her arms
and kiss him, but she did not do that. She only
kissed his hand. He thanked her in his execrable
French for looking after his bride and also for looking after Josephine some years previously. As he
said the words *l'Impératrice Joséphine*, he fetched a
deep Italian sigh, and Madame Clare formed the
impression that he still loved Josephine and had
only divorced her to get an heir, and was not happy
at the prospect of living with this proud daughter
of the Hapsburgs. He and Josephine had suited
each other so well in the old days, the gay Creole
and the little officer of artillery, both of about the
same class with the same bourgeois outlook on life.
But when grandeur had been thrust upon her Josephine had played her part to perfection, and made a
far more dignified Empress than he an Emperor.

Now she was living quietly at Malmaison, cultivating the roses, which were named after her. 'Pray for me,' said the Emperor abruptly, and turned away.

This was the climax of Madame Clare's life and the next year she died, having reigned as Abbess for nearly forty years. She died murmuring, '*Priez pour moi, pauvre pécheresse.*'

6

THE COMMUNITY quietly prospered during the nineteenth century. Its doings were much less spectacular than during the eighteenth century, not that the
nineteenth was a much less spectacular epoch. The
life of the nuns was more austere, more in keeping
with the Rule of St Benedict. They were no longer
entertained in houses in the town, though they could
still be met with, walking two by two along the
shady boulevards. But the emphasis now was on
education and they opened a school where languages,
literature, handicrafts, logic, and simple arithmetic
were taught. They were respected, even loved, by
the people of Soissons to whom they had by now
become as permanent a feature of the city as the
Cathedral itself. The various revolutions in Paris,
the July Revolution, the Revolution of 1848, and
the revolution which culminated in the Second
Empire, scarcely affected them at all. Napoleon III
and Eugénie spent a great deal of time at Compiègne but they were not religiously inclined and
never came to Soissons. The Abbess Elizabeth once
saw Napoleon III but was far less impressed than

her predecessor had been by his uncle. A shoddy little man she thought him and she did not like his bandy legs.

Nothing stirred the quiet waters of their life until the beginning of the twentieth century and the Drey-fus case. Then the waters began to boil and bubble. When the Catholics had thoroughly discredited themselves by their obstinate anti-Semitism and support of a bigoted General Staff, along came Émile Combes, who passed the anti-religious laws, and the monks and nuns were expelled from France. The Abbess at the time was the Abbess Léonie, a rather weak little woman, small, delicate, and as a rule somewhat ineffectual. But this time she rose to the occasion like a lioness. She went to Paris and she sat in Monsieur Combes's waiting-room, though told that she could not possibly see him, until he came out. What about the school? she asked him. It was not a religious school. Its curriculum was wholly secular. The town of Soissons had also risen to the occasion. The Ladies of Soissons were by now an institution, a feature, of their city, quite apart from their religious value. Hardened anti-clericals and agnostics signed the monster petition which had already been sent to Monsieur Combes, threatening all kinds of reprisals if their Ladies were sent away. Monsieur Combes did not want any more riots and disturbances. There had been enough already. The petition lay on his table a few yards away though the

Abbess did not know it. He had looked at it. Had she known she would have been less surprised than she was when he said, rather wearily, that she and her nuns could stay, on two conditions: one, that they remained strictly enclosed and were not seen and their chapel closed to the public; and, two, that if necessity forced herself or any of her nuns to leave the precincts of the convent, they were to go dressed in lay clothes.

The Abbess thanked him and went away quickly before he could change his mind. Thus, the Ladies of Soissons were the only religious Community to remain in France. The Abbess quickly designed some suitable lay clothes: black hat with a short veil, black coat and skirt with white collar and cuffs, black gloves, shoes and stockings; and the nuns, looking like respectable widows, continued to parade the town as usual. The citizens of Soissons were immensely proud, first and especially, of having routed the Government, a feat so dear to the heart of every Frenchman always, and secondly, of having retained their beloved Ladies.

7

IN THE year 1906 the Abbess Léonie died and the
greatest event in the history of the Community took
place, though no one realised it at the time, not even
the authors of it: a young woman of thirty, Catherine
Allières, was elected Abbess and became the 'Great
Abbess', Catherine the Great, as she was called by
the nuns behind her back. She reigned till 1956,
when she abdicated, after celebrating her Jubilee as
Abbess, in favour of the present Abbess Eileen, as
has already been told in a previous chapter. She
reigned through the anti-clerical period, the 1914–18
war, and the last war; she was exiled twice; she was
decorated, with the troops forming a hollow square
around her, and later returned her decorations; she
fought with Bishops and Cardinals, and won; and
with a Primitive Methodist officer of the British
Army, and lost; and she lives, a revered old lady of
85, in a convent on the outskirts of Paris with
leisure to think of it all.

Until 1914 she faithfully observed her predecessor's pact with Monsieur Combes. Indeed she went
further, for she allowed no one to leave the convent

save on urgent business or to visit doctor or dentist. She thought it would not be a bad thing if, after their two centuries of comparative laxity, they used this opportunity to practise for a while the primitive Rule of St Benedict. This notion proved fortunate for when the war broke out in 1914, they were a calm, disciplined body ready to face whatever the future might bring.

It brought a violent change in their existence. Immediately war broke out the Abbess Catherine went up to Paris, and waited in Monsieur Clémenceau's ante-room just as her predecessor had waited in the ante-room of Monsieur Combes. She had to wait six hours but she would not budge. At last Clémenceau appeared. 'What do you want?' he said abruptly, scarcely stopping and perhaps hoping to escape. But the young Abbess (and it is curious that everyone always thinks of the Great Abbess as permanently old and venerable, when during the most spectacular part of her reign she was neither, but still in her thirties) was already between him and the door.

'*Monsieur le Ministre*,' she said, 'We want to fight, *pour la patrie*. We can settle our religious differences when the war is over. *À cet instant la France est en danger*. The fighting history of our Community is a fine one. We fought as hospital nurses with our King James Stuart in 1688 and two of us were killed by cannon shot at the Battle of the Boyne. The Boche is

49

already near Soissons. It will soon be in the front line. Permit us to go as a hospital unit to the *poilus* with a field ambulance, and care for the wounded before they are sent down to the base.'

Clémenceau, the hater of nuns, stared at this determined young woman. Then after a pause he said '*Bon*. To the front. But nursing only, mind you! No religion!'

'*Le salut de la France est ma religion*,' said the Abbess, '*parce que si la France tomberait, ce serait aussi la chute de la religion*.'

'*Et le Rocher de St Pierre?*' queried Clémenceau with a twinkle in his eye. 'I fear if your superiors were to hear you, they would sniff heresy. It is lucky you are speaking to an unbeliever.'

'France is the eldest daughter of the Church, *Monsieur le Ministre*. The Church could ill spare her eldest daughter, whom she needs to look after her. That is not heresy, *Monsieur* . . . though not strict orthodoxy either!' The Abbess laughed, a wonderfully fresh, spontaneous laugh. '*Merci, Monsieur*,' she said. '*À bientôt!* For *Monsieur* will be at the front himself before long, I am certain, and perhaps we shall meet.'

'I sincerely hope so, Madame, and good luck.'

He shook hands with her gravely, and she left the room, treading on air.

Some weeks later she received a military movement order telling her to report, together with her nuns, to the Commandant of the 14th Field Hospital at Brèves near Soissons. They hurriedly packed up the convent and left it to the pensionnaires, care-takers and the good God to look after, and went up the line.

For seven months they were under shell-fire. None of them were killed but several were wounded. Then the French withdrew, and that section of the western front was taken over by the British. The Abbess duly reported to her new commanding officer.

'Who the hell are you?' he said. 'Nuns? French? The Ladies of Soissons? What does it all mean? In any case I don't want any nuns here, nor does the RAMC bloke, I'm quite sure. Don't know how to nurse, always praying at the men and trying to con-vert them. I'm a Presbyterian meself. I don't trust the Romish Church, not as far as I can see it. In any case we have our own nurses, properly trained women from Edinburgh. You will report back to me at 4 a.m. tomorrow when arrangements will have been made to send you down the line. Good day to you!' He started riffling through his papers and would not give her another look.

The Abbess was beaten, cowed, by this ferocious, red-haired Presbyterian savage. Throughout the conversation, she had not opened her mouth. It was the first and the last time in her long life that she suffered defeat, and it taught her a lesson which she never forgot, namely, take the offensive immediately and hit hard with all you've got, every verbal argument, every threat, persuasion, cajolement, promise, tears, laughter, rhetoric, plain quiet fact. Don't let your opponent get a word in edgeways. She invariably employed this technique on later occasions, and Bishops, Cardinals, officials of all kinds, both clerical and lay, went down before her like ninepins.

The next day their horses and two carts were waiting outside the nuns' tents. Shell-fire was heavy. They climbed into the carts and were driven slowly away over rough shell-pitted tracks down to the base where they were put in a train and after fourteen hours with nothing to eat or drink (though the troops, all British, for it was a 'Blighty' leave train, got plenty), they arrived at Le Havre.

A nun was waiting on the platform. She introduced herself unsmilingly as the Prioress of a Benedictine house near the quays, and said Movement Control had sent her a telegram warning her to be ready to receive the Abbess of Soissons and her Community.

'I am afraid it will not be at all what you are used to, Madame,' said the Prioress. 'We are a poor little house. We run a school for fishermen's children and we do some work among the poor, but we are very poor ourselves, and I really don't know how we are going to fit in. How am I going to find room for sixty nuns? I am indeed glad you did not come in your coach and carriages. What we would have done with *them*, the good God only knows.'

Abbess Catherine reflected sadly that she would never see horse, coach or carriage again, but she did, for the unpredictable British, always kinder to animals than humans, sent them to safe-keeping near Paris and they were restored to the Community in 1919. Why they were not allowed to travel in them the Abbess never discovered.

It was autumn. Cold winds blew in from the sea. The Abbess hired a complete block of flats overlooking the harbour and made of that her convent. There was a church just round the corner, which served as their chapel. They advertised that they gave lessons in dancing and deportment, mathematics, literature, logic, elementary philosophy.

But the Abbess was miserable. Here they were, refugees from the war, all fit and able to fight. She used to wander with her secretary Dame Ybru over the sands, watching the troopships passing in and out of the harbour. 'It is like a picture by Boudin,' she sighed. 'What can we do? I hate this place which is virtually an English camp. I hate the boors just as much as they hate us. The good God permits one to hate what is evil. They have no manners at all. In any case I don't intend that either I or my nuns shall sit here twiddling our fingers for years until the Yankees have come over and won the war for us.

I shall go and see Clémenceau. He is Prime Minister now. He might remember me. If he doesn't I'll remind him.'

To get to Paris she had to have an order from British Movement Control. She was apparently living in a 'restricted area'. She let fly at the unfortunate Movement Control Officer, a Kitchener's Army volunteer who had never seen a nun before. '*Sapristi! Ventre Saint Gris! Tonnerre! Parbleu, mais c'est trop fort!* Do I, a Frenchwoman, have to ask permission from an English officer to go to Paris, my Paris?'

'In wartime, yes, miss.'

'*Diable! C'est insupportable!* Then give it me, the filthy piece of paper, at once,'

'I don't know as 'ow I ought.'

'Give it me, this instant, then get out of here and get out of Havre, out of France, all of you, all you foul English, and let us beat the Boche in our own way. You have always been the enemy since the Hundred Years' War.'

She snatched the pass out of his hand before he could stop her and whirled out of the room. He mopped his brow.

'These bloody natives,' he exclaimed. 'Always so excitable.'

8

ONCE AGAIN the Abbess Catherine waited in Clémenceau's ante-room, but this time it was at the Palais Bourbon and this time she had an appointment, for the Premier remembered her.

He greeted her almost affectionately. 'You did great things up on the Aisne,' he said. 'You are all mentioned in despatches. I wish you could have stayed there. These damned English will lose us the war. They would have done so already if it had not been for Lloyd George, a Welshman. As to these Frenches and Haigs, and Henry Wilsons, their ignorance of modern warfare is abysmal. When they invent a useful new weapon like the tank, they won't use it. Impossible people. Would you like to go to Verdun?'

'Where is that, *Monsieur le Premier Ministre?*'

'In the Vosges, or thereabouts. Not an important section of the line at present, but for that very reason they need field nurses because the fighting fronts have drawn all the field hospital units away. But if Joffre's autumn push fails, then . . . why then

Verdun will become a hell on earth, because that's where the Germans will try and break through.'

'Good! Let us go quickly then to Verdun.'

So to Verdun they went, and it was cold they suffered from most in the tents at night up at those heights. The line was very quiet: desultory shelling, accidents, self-mutilations, but no wounded.

But Joffre's push failed and down came the Germans to Verdun in a counter-attack, like a swarm of bees. The place was turned into a fortress and the field hospital transferred to the dungeons of one of Vauban's old forts deep underground.

The nuns did not like this. They preferred to see what was happening. The Abbess arranged for parties of them to accompany the wounded on their dangerous overland journey through an inferno of bombardment down to the base. They made the return journey each day with relieving troops in lorries. Three nuns were killed. Eight were wounded. The Abbess herself made the trip as often as she could. The presence of these nuns was a source of great moral help to the *poilus*. Just as they had become in Soissons in more peaceful times a symbol of something, people hardly knew what, a kind of mascot, so that even the anti-clericals had petitioned against their expulsion, so now, at Verdun, they became a kind of talisman for the soldiers, no matter how contemptuous of religion many of them may have been. '*Si les bonnes soeurs nous accom-*

pagnent, nous arriverons sains et saufs,' they used to say, and, no matter how violent the shelling, would lie quietly on the stretchers as long as one of the nuns was walking beside them. To one and all of them the Abbess was a kind of goddess. Her quick wit, her gift of repartee, her sense of humour, her courage and evident patriotism, her deep religious faith, her splendid character and presence, endeared her to all, officers and men.

At last the tide of battle receded. *'Ils ne passeront pas,'* the French soldiers had said, nor had they. One cold blustery morning, in the most beautiful square in Europe, the Place Stanislaus at Nancy, built by a Polish king who was also a Duke of Lorraine, one of the recovered provinces, the infantry were forming a hollow square prior to some solemn ceremony which was to be enacted. Crowds lined the barriers behind the troops and filled the stately eighteenth-century palaces round the square. At noon a band played the 'Marseillaise', trumpets blew, flags were unfurled, and on to the parade ground marched General Pétain and a glittering staff. At the opposite end of the square, huddled together against the cold wind and trying to prevent their veils from being blown across their faces, was a group of nuns, looking very small against this vast and imposing background of palaces, soldiers in ceremonial uniform, crowds, bands, and generals in full dress wearing orders and decorations.

There was a moment's silence, and then a voice rang out: 'Madame Catherine Allières, Lady Abbess of the Benedictines of Soissons!'

The Abbess emerged from the group and in complete silence made her dignified crossing of the great square to where General Pétain was waiting with his staff. She felt her knees trembling and it seemed several kilometres of empty windy space that she must cross, and the silent crowd like so many jungle animals waiting to pounce, but there was no outward sign of this in her demeanour as she walked across the square with a grace and dignity worthy of her great contemporaries on the stage, Bernhardt and Réjane.

She stood before General Pétain at last, clasping her veil which kept floating out behind her on the wind. The General stepped forward. The drums rumbled a greeting and the trumpets sounded a fanfare. '*Vous avez bien mérité de la patrie, Madame,*' said Pétain and pinned the Croix de Guerre with palms and the Pour le Mérite Cross upon the Abbess's breast, the first, and last, woman ever to receive these battle honours. Then Pétain, a good Catholic, knelt down and kissed her ring before standing up and giving her the traditional accolade on both cheeks. '*C'est la première fois que j'ai embrassé une religieuse,*' he said with a twinkle in his eye, '*et maintenant, voyez-vous, je l'ai fait trois fois de suite!*'

The silence was now broken by a roar of applause

from the crowd, as if the jungle beasts were suddenly loose and on the prowl. The Abbess, with tears in her eyes and a superhuman effort towards self-control, turned and gestured towards the little group of her nuns, huddled away there across the vast square. *'C'est pour elles!'* she kept exclaiming, pointing to the medals on her breast. She saw that they were all waving their handkerchiefs and umbrellas and cheering her with the crowd. She bowed to the General, and, turning, walked slowly back to join them, very slowly in order not to lose her dignity by falling down, for her knees had gone to jelly and she could feel her heart beating and her pulse fluttering. As soon as she reached the shelter of the group, who surrounded her, congratulating, and hid her from the crowd, she broke down and wept violently. 'Oh, my children, my children! God is vindicated in His own good time! Ten years ago there were no religious in France except ourselves, and now the army and the whole people of this liberated city turn out with ceremony to watch a community of nuns receive the two highest battle honours to be won in France!'

9

THE RETURN of the Community to Soissons was a
scene of wild rejoicing, exceeding that of their return from Aachen over a century before. That had
been a return from flight and this a return from
fight. There was a difference.

They found the convent half ruined by shell-fire
and neglect, but every tradesman and craftsman in
the town and every gardener and market gardener,
and every plasterer and painter, and every artist, and
every priest, turned to and helped them, and in a
few years the convent looked much as it had done
previously and the chapel was reconsecrated and in
use.

The Abbess Catherine was middle-aged now, inclined to stoutness, but a fine figure of a woman still,
and like all the Abbesses of Soissons, whether good
or bad, a figure of consummate dignity. Her normal
expression was mild and benevolent, but she was
capable of irony, sarcasm, plain anger, and a quiet
disapproval which her nuns found the most frighten-
ing of all. She was, of course, a famous heroine from
one end of France to the other, and was always

being asked to preside over this and that, to take the Chair here and there, to speak at such and such a banquet. She invariably refused.

'We must devote much time to prayer,' she said. 'Praying hard and unceasingly for France that she may be spared the even worse horrors that seem to be in store for her in the near future.'

For Soissons is not far from the German frontier. One of the few excursions the Abbess had made was to Paderborn in Germany where the sexennial congress of Mitred Abbesses was held. These princely ladies came from all parts of Germany, from Hungary, Poland, Austria, Italy, Spain, and one from England. They were entertained by their opposite numbers, the Prince-Bishops of the Rhineland, and welcomed by the older people of the district. But it was noticed that most of the young people, many of whom wore brown shirts or were in storm trooper's uniform, were openly hostile, and it was widely known that the Führer had said that never again would he allow a meeting of these meddlesome religious to be held within the frontiers of the Third Reich.

The Abbess returned to Soissons downcast, and ordered her nuns to make a novena for peace.

But there was no peace, and in 1940, when the Abbess had passed her sixtieth birthday, the Germans invaded France. All through the previous winter of the 'phoney war', the Abbess had sent her nuns in batches to take courses in nursing which were being held at Rheims. When the war of movement began, therefore, her nuns were up in the front line at once, trained, with their tents and field hospital, headed by their Abbess.

But they had not been there long when the French Army quietly melted away! One day they were there, with the Belgians not far away. The next day all were gone.

'Well, I'm not going to be taken prisoner by the Boche and spend years locked up in some stuffy German convent,' declared the Abbess. 'The army has gone, and we will go also.' She still had no idea that the army had *run* away, because French soldiers in her day did not do such things. She merely thought the new Generalissimo Weygand, a friend of her beloved Pétain, had some rapid and brilliant manœuvre in mind and that HQ had omitted to inform them of their departure.

But when the Community got on to the roads and saw the streams of refugees and noticed how many men in uniform were among them, they began to have doubts, though to doubt the superiority over all others of the French Army was almost like doubting the existence of God.

Suddenly into the chaos came the sound of troops marching with regular step, of orders given, of disciplined soldiers approaching. Their hearts rose. General Weygand's strategy had succeeded. Those men in uniform we saw on the road were just a few stragglers who had lost their units.

But the troops were British. Abbess Catherine, remembering her treatment in the previous war, twenty-five years before, at the hands of the British, viewed them a little doubtfully. However, they were obviously a resolute band of men come there to fight the Germans, so she turned and followed them. They made for Soissons! The nuns had been all this while not far from home, for their field hospital had been situated at Brèves only eight miles outside the town. The Abbess immediately hurried up to the commanding officer, a colonel, and offered him the convent buildings as a billet.

He was about to answer her rather abruptly, and to say that his billeting officer had already arranged all that, when he saw the two ribbons on her breast.

'Excuse me, Madame, but I see you are wearing the Croix de Guerre with palms and the Pour le Mérite Cross.' He looked perplexed. He was a stickler for professional etiquette in matters such as the correct wearing of medals. 'Is it in memory of some relative that you wear them, though you shouldn't ? They are pretty things,' he added half to himself. He collected medals of the period of the Peninsular War.

'I won them at the Battle of Verdun, *mon Colonel,*' said the Abbess, 'or rather my gallant nuns won them and I, as their Abbess, wear them. As you rightly say, I should not. They should.'

'Who gave them you?'

'Field-Marshal Pétain, *mon Colonel.*'

'He is to be head of the new Government, did you know?'

The Abbess's face lit up. '*Mais non!* I did not know. Oh, then France is saved.'

'I don't know about that. The Government is a long way off, at Bordeaux, and rumour has it they are going to North Africa. Do you know what we are here for?'

'To fight Germans, I hope,' said the Abbess.

'Yes, of course, but only in a rearguard action, to cover the retreat of the French Army and our own to the coast, where we hope to give them time to embark for England.'

'The French Army evacuating France?' The Abbess was thunderstruck.

'Yes. Some to England, some to North Africa, hoping to live and fight another day. A certain Colonel de Gaulle is going to organise a Free French Fighting Force in London.'

'*La France abandonnée par des Français! Impossible!*' declared the Abbess. 'What, then, can we do? We are a field hospital unit, with fully trained nurses. We have fought in this war, and in the last, and we started fighting at the Battle of the Boyne in 1690.'

'Good heavens!' said the colonel, who spoke

excellent idiomatic French with a strong English accent, and who used to spend his leave in France on gastronomic tours before the war and was therefore a civilised person. 'What a record! So you came from England originally?'

'Yes, though we are now completely French. When King James II had been to Scotland and failed to make the rising known as the '15, he departed for Rome where he remained, and we came under the protection of King Louis XIV and became affiliated to the French Congregation of Benedictines.'

'Well now,' said the colonel, 'I'm glad you told me this because now I can make a suggestion. You can, of course, stay here in France. The Germans, almost certainly, are going to occupy the country, not just Paris as in 1870, but the whole of France, and Pétain is going to be forced to come to some sort of accommodation with them. They will not, I think, molest you and your nuns, but there will be no fighting for you. There will be nothing you can do towards the liberation of your country. If you want to fight, if you want the chance to form again a field ambulance unit, you must come to the only place left where Frenchmen are preparing to fight, preparing for the day when they will return and liberate their country.'

'You mean, go to England, *mon Colonel?*'

'I mean just that. It is highly irregular, but I have some influence and I think I can get you on to a

E

fishing boat which will take you across the Channel and land you in England.'

'*Quitter la France . . . ah, mais c'est dur.*'

'Is it harder than to watch France helpless beneath the feet of the invader, of the Boche, to see Hitler and Goering strutting down the Champs-Élysées?'

The Abbess hid her face in her hands. 'No,' she said in a strangled voice, 'it is not harder. And do you really think we shall come back? And soon?'

'I don't know how soon, but sooner or later, yes, you will come back and the Third Reich will be utterly destroyed. Norwegians, Dutch, Poles, Frenchmen, they have all come to join us in England. We have our New Zealanders, Australians, Canadians, South Africans. The Americans are making things for us that we need. We command the sea and we shall soon command the air. Germany, so triumphant at present, is doomed.'

'Very well, I come with you, *mon Colonel*, I go to your country, but on the understanding that I come back and fight.'

He smiled at this fierce old lady and her vehemence, and kissed her hand. 'Come with me,' he said.

IO

So THE Abbess and her nuns embarked on a fishing boat at Honfleur for England, just as their predecessors had embarked in a fishing boat at Westport in Mayo for France. The colonel, in his admiration of the woman, had moved heaven and earth, meaning Whitehall, which functions as both in time of war, and arrangements had been made for the Community to be accommodated on arrival in England. They were to go to a convent of Benedictine nuns in Middlesex. 'That's where they started from a couple of centuries and more ago; that's where they had better go back to,' said Whitehall.

If she had not been so upset at the turn of events in France, almost mentally paralysed with shock, the Abbess would have enjoyed the voyage in the practically open fishing boat to England. The strong tides of the Channel plus a strong breeze caused short steep seas, and the boat lurched up and down, and stood first on its head and then on its tail. Most of the nuns were desperately ill, but the Abbess, whose first experience of a sea voyage this was, had no qualms whatever. Firmly wedged on deck in a spot selected for her by the skipper, she sat hour after hour motionless, sometimes reading her office, but not until the coast of France was out of sight astern, and often gazing out upon the waste of waters, where now and then another boat, also carrying refugees to England, would appear. Of aeroplanes, whether Allied or German, she saw no sign. They were all over Dunkirk.

The feeling of remoteness which usually accompanies a voyage out of sight of land assailed her. She seemed to be suspended between earth and heaven, between a new life and the old. Something made her doubt if she ever would fight again, or even see France again. 'This is a much more terrible war than the last,' she told herself.

At last the lights of the Isle of Wight and the Needles lighthouse came into view, and later, in a cold damp dawn, they were sailing up Southampton Water and the Abbess was looking at England for the first time. Her first impressions were not disagreeable. It looked trim, neat, relaxed, comfortable. The docks at Southampton were sleepy in the early morning light. Little work seemed to be going on. Officials were waiting for her at the docks. They were given permits to land and told to present themselves to the local police station on arrival. They drove up to London in two comfortable buses and the chief impression they got, after the terrible confusion and misery of France, was that England was not at war at all. The orderly quiet, the normality, was that of a country still at peace. '*C'est à cause de la mer qu'ils peuvent se ficher ainsi d'Hitler,*' the Abbess informed her nuns gravely. They believed her. None of them, had they twice the power and might of Hitler, would have crossed that sea again for any reason whatsoever. They had never felt so ill, and so ashamedly ill, in their lives, and they were privately determined that they would liberate their country by air when the day came.

Three hours later, about 9 a.m., they arrived at the Priory. Most of them had no idea where they were. 'This is your home,' the Abbess explained, with a trace of irony in her voice. 'This is where we started from in 1688. It was from here we fled to France, via Ireland.'

The Prioress, who had been notified of their arrival by the War Office only late the night before and was at her wits' end where to put them, received them somewhat ungraciously.

'I don't know who you are or where you come from,' she said. 'I suppose you are French. All I have been told is that I have to look after you, and where I am going to put you or how I am going to feed you, I simply don't know. You will have to go to the Town Hall after you have been to the police station and get ration cards.'

The Abbess, whose English was not very good, only understood half the woman said. In her inner

69

ear she still heard the persistent and melancholy wailing of the gulls, which had seemed to her, as she listened to them off the Needles, like the souls of all the French men and women who would be lost during this war.

'Where we come from,' she said. She pulled herself together, trying to be dignified and amiable. 'We come from here,' she gave an ingratiating little laugh. 'We left here for France with King James II in 1688, and we have been abroad ever since.'

'Ah! You were the ones who ratted!' exclaimed the Prioress.

'Ratted? What means ratted?' said the Abbess.

'How did a convent manage to exist at all at such a date, in England?' asked the Prioress suspiciously and omitting completely to enlighten the Abbess on the subject of 'ratting'.

'Because King James II was a Catholic, openly, and his brother and predecessor on the throne, Charles II, secretly. Before that, in the days of Cromwell, we were governesses in Catholic houses, serving maids, anything. When Henrietta Maria was Queen to Charles I we came out of hiding, but before that we were in hiding and disguise from Elizabeth. During her sister Mary's reign we were a Priory once more, but suppressed by King Henry VIII. We were founded in 1140 and flourished until the Reformation. You see, I tell you your own history backwards!' She gave another little laugh.

The Prioress became a little more gracious. A look almost of admiration crept into her eyes. For these were the true descendants of the Priory and she beheld them with awe as the inheritors of an immensely long tradition. They themselves had only been formed after the passing of the Catholic Emancipation Bill at the beginning of the nineteenth century. They were really interlopers, and this made the Prioress's position still more awkward. She was inferior to the Abbess in rank, this was not her rightful home, the Abbess and her Community were refugees, and yet her first duty was towards the welfare of her own Community, that it be not disturbed.

The Abbess guessed something of what was passing through her mind. 'We shall not be here long,' she said. 'We are shortly going off to fight, when the Free French invade their own country,' she laughed, bitterly this time.

'Fight!' exclaimed the Prioress. 'Nuns don't fight!'

'These do!' exclaimed the Abbess. 'They fought in Ireland in 1688, after Sedan in 1870, in 1914, at Verdun, where I received these on behalf of the Community' (she drew back the folds of her cloak and revealed her ribbons sewn on to her habit), 'and in this war we have fought until now.'

'How "fought"?' asked the astonished Prioress.

'Field Ambulance Unit,' said the Abbess tersely.

'Well, well,' was all the Prioress, completely at a loss by now, could find to say.

II

Life proved exceedingly uncomfortable at the Priory. The Abbess Catherine was quite certain they would not be able to stand it much longer. '*Ce n'est pas convenable pour les Dames de Soissons,*' was a complaint she frequently heard. It made her angry. 'There is a war on,' she told her nuns, 'and you must muck in like everyone else.' (The Abbess's English was apt to be startling, since she had picked it up from listening to the troops at Le Havre during the first war.) 'It is inconvenient,' she continued, 'but it is perfectly *convenable*.'

'These *dortoirs*,' moaned the nuns. At Soissons each had had a room to herself. 'And the food!'

The food was indeed disgusting, the Abbess agreed. Not only was it rationed but it was vilely cooked and unappetisingly served, with nearly everything, if it were meat or fish, drowned in a foul concoction called Winchester Sauce, or if it were 'pouding' drowned in an even viler concoction called custard.

One day the climax was reached.

'*Qu'est-ce que c'est?*' inquired the Abbess gazing sadly at her plate.

'Spotted dog,' answered the Prioress.

The Abbess gave an eldritch shriek like an express train entering a tunnel, and rising to her feet, '*Ne mangez pas, mes enfants,*' she cried. '*N'y touchez pas! ... Venez!*'

Outside the refectory she explained to her horrified nuns that the British were so short of food that they had just been offered spotted dog, *c'est à dire*, dogs with *la petite vérole*, who had had to be killed off . . . and no, they must never eat in this convent again. They would be poisoned. She thereupon gave her nuns permission to go, two by two, to Antionelli's Italian Restaurant in the High Street where the food was pure.

Signor Antionelli was a good Catholic and soon came to an arrangement with the Abbess by which her nuns dined and lunched for a fixed price in a private room upstairs, and he saw to it that they each had a half bottle of wine each day to drink. Nevertheless the French nuns eating in a restaurant caused terrible scandal among the Catholics of Middlesex.

It was nothing, however, compared to the furore when they went to the cinema, where a French film was being shown.

'Was it edifying?' the Abbess was asked.

'Indeed, yes,' replied the Abbess. 'We learned

73

things which I never imagined existed in all the world . . . habits, rather. It was about "ladies" who follow the troops to the front . . . *vivandières*, I think they are called.'

'I cannot have this,' said the Prioress to herself. 'The situation is becoming intolerable.'

'What do you expect us to do?' asked the Abbess that evening when the subject was broached. She had just returned, discouraged, from a visit to the Free French Headquarters, where they held out no hope of her Community's being required to form a field ambulance unit as yet. 'We are far from ready to leave this country,' they had said, 'not trained, no weapons, no plans . . .'

'St Benedict,' she observed to the Prioress, 'divided our time into *Laborare et Orare*. We cannot pray *all* the time. We do say our office, add many extra prayers, make novenas, spend long hours on our knees in chapel, but we must have some work to do as well. It is not healthy otherwise. But if there is no work, we go to the cinema. What would you, Madame? We cannot sit and twiddle our fingers when we have exhausted our prayers. Give us work, I pray you . . . teaching French, sewing, making bandages, anything . . . work in the fields even, hoeing, haymaking, growing vegetables, picking fruit.'

'Alas!' wailed the Prioress. 'I wish I could, but I don't see my way to set about it.'

'Feckless woman,' thought the Abbess. 'Do you not understand how desperate it is for my nuns,' she said. 'They don't know a word of your language and none of your nuns speak French. They would like to be friends, of course.'

'Oh, no! They think they are too grand for us! The Ladies of Soissons! All Dames indeed. And you expecting people to kneel and kiss your ring! Well, as far as this country is concerned, you'll go on expecting!'

'There is no need to be rude,' said the Abbess and left the room.

The Prioress rushed to the telephone and got on to the secretary of a prelate who occasionally visited the convent.

'This cannot continue,' she cried. 'These nuns must go. They are corrupting my poor girls with their immodest French ways. They go to the cinema, they eat in restaurants, they laugh and chatter in public on walks, they laze about on seats in the public gardens, they give themselves great airs, especially Madame Catherine, and they must go!'

The result of this was a visit from a Bishop.

The Prioress introduced them and discreetly withdrew. The Abbess's secretary sat taking shorthand notes in a dark corner. It was Madame Catherine's invariable rule that whenever any conversation likely to affect the future of the convent took place, Madame Ybru should take shorthand notes of it.

The Bishop stood waiting in silence, his hand on which glittered the episcopal ring outstretched. The Abbess similarly stood, her hand also outstretched, and also decorated with a glittering ring.

'It is for you to kneel to me, Monseigneur,' said the Abbess quietly. Nothing like demoralising your opponent from the start.

'I beg your pardon,' cried the startled Bishop. 'Since when do I have to kneel to a woman?'

'Since the fifth century, Monseigneur, a Bishop kneels to a Mitred Abbess.'

'Good heavens! To a what?'

'A Mitred Abbess, sir.'

'Never heard of them.'

'Well, there are plenty about. There is one in England at Stanbrook. They possess the privileges, but not the powers, of a Prince-Bishop.'

'A what?'

'A Prince-Bishop . . . like Trier, Speyer, Mainz.'

'Oh! Germans! We don't have Prince-Bishops in England.'

For a moment the Abbess lost her temper. 'Oh, you don't have anything in England . . . I know that. No food, no civilisation, no religion . . . that I know . . . But you have a Prince-Bishop . . . at Durham.'

'How in heaven's name do you know?'

'I have been reading books in the Prioress's dreary library because I have nothing better to do,' said the Abbess. 'I pray fourteen hours a day but I can't do more than that.'

The two antagonists glared at one another. Then the Abbess burst into her full, rich laugh. 'Let us both sit down,' she said, 'and neither kneel to the other, and compose ourselves for our discussion. Dame Ybru, some tea for the Bishop.'

They sat down facing one another and Madame Ybru returned almost immediately with the tea which the Prioress had been preparing for His Lordship, and also with a half bottle of white wine.

'This is my tipple,' announced the Abbess waving the bottle aloft in front of the startled Bishop. 'My English not right,' she added seeing his face go red. 'You must excuse me. I learnt it with the British Tommies in the 1914 war.'

'What were you doing with the British Tommies in the First World War?' intoned the bewildered Bishop.

She told him. She gave him a succinct account of the doings of the Ladies of Soissons during the last two hundred and fifty years. He began to admire her. They were by now much better friends.

'But you must find us a temporary home,' she concluded. 'We are much too crowded up here. There simply is not room. We must have a home where we can live as a Community and follow the Rule. It will only be temporary, for as soon as we are ready, we French I mean, they will send for us to go and fight.'

The Bishop had not the heart to tell this gallant old woman that her fighting days were done (she was 65); and that, without their Abbess to manage things, the Community would never be allowed to go out nursing at the front on its own.

'I will see if we can find you somewhere,' he said, 'but meanwhile, until you hear from me again, I shall be obliged if you do not go to the cinema."

They shook hands and parted on the most friendly terms.

It was about three weeks later that Madame Catherine received a summons to an audience with a very high-ranking prelate indeed.

The Bishop was apprehensive about this. He warned his superior that she was an extraordinary woman, who evidently had long enjoyed a unique reputation in France and, both on account of this and on account of the fact that she was a Mitred Abbess, was accustomed to a degree of deference which we, in this country, were not accustomed to bestow. Also that she had learnt English from the Tommies in the 1914 war, and His Grace must not be shocked by some of the things she said.

'Not a bit,' said the Archbishop. 'It will give me nostalgia for my days as an army chaplain in that same war.'

The Bishop then tried to explain about Mitred

Abbesses and their pretensions, but the Archbishop cut him short.

'I know all about them, my dear fellow,' he said. 'I have come across a number of them in various places, and a formidable set of ladies they are. I am glad there are not more of them. Yours sounds to be a typical example.'

At that moment Madame Catherine, followed by her discreet shadow, Dame Ybru, with notebook and pencil, was ushered into the Presence. The Bishop held his breath.

She went straight down on both knees at the Archbishop's feet, and humbly kissed his ring. He looked over her bent head at the Bishop and winked. She was going to be tractable.

He raised her to her feet. '*Ah, Monseigneur!*' she cried. '*Comme il est bon de vous voir!*'

The Archbishop returned her compliment in perfect French, idiomatic and correct, but with a strong British accent. He was very fond of France and spent his holidays there.

'Come and sit down,' he said and led her to a chair. The Bishop also sat, with a sigh of relief. Dame Ybru, in the shadows, licked her pencil.

'I have ordered some of your own "tipple", ' he said as a servant brought in two glasses and a bottle of wine. 'Tea's coming up for you, old man,' he said to the Bishop. 'I know you're not a wine bibber. I confess I am when I get the chance.'

'*Eh bien*,' he said to the Abbess, 'I have good news for you. I have a house for you, a large house, a beautiful house, a château.'

'*Ah, Monseigneur, comme vous êtes bon!*' Impulsively the Abbess got to her feet and for a moment he thought she was going to kiss him . . . indeed, that was what she meant to do, but checked herself in time and seizing his hands kissed them instead, one after the other. The Bishop held his breath for a moment, then let out a sigh of relief.

'This beautiful château is in Ireland,' continued the Archbishop.

For a moment, the Abbess was too stupefied to do anything but gasp. Then she gave vent to a prolonged wail, of such power and intensity as to bring the chaplain hurrying in, convinced either that the Abbess had fainted or that the Bishop in a moment of uncontrollable exasperation had murdered her.

'*Irelande!*' she howled. '*La fin du monde! . . . Pays brutal et inconnu!* Forgotten! We shall be forgotten! And is not Ireland neutral? How can we fight from Ireland?'

The Archbishop handed her the wine glass. She took a pull at its contents and felt better.

'It is an astonishing piece of luck,' he continued. 'I was at my wits' end where to put you when . . . truly, the finger of God is in it . . . I received a letter from a very famous singer, a great Catholic. Many years ago, one of our English millionaires built this mansion in Ireland. He lavished on it vast sums of money. It has lakes stocked with trout, it has the finest arboretum in the country, it has its own sea bathing, and many farms and cottages and properties of all kinds, as well as a large church in the grounds where he intended that he and all his descendants should be buried. Well, he overspent himself and went bankrupt, and the famous singer bought the property for a song . . . oh dear, I did not intend that obvious facetiousness . . . he now finds, poor fellow, that he is dying. He had to cancel a concert because of a sore throat and thought it was laryngitis, and it proved to be cancer. He has not long to live and has no heirs, so has made the generous gift of this mansion to any religious community in need of it, preferably one driven from its home by the war. The Cardinal in Ireland could find no applicants, so wrote to me, and I immediately thought of you, and have wired him to say that you are coming.'

'But Ireland . . . we cannot go to Ireland.'

'Why not? Some connoisseurs of such things say it is the most beautiful country in the world.'

'But one cannot live on scenery.'

'The food is excellent. The Irish are great gastronomes. The butter and the cheese, to name only two things, are of superb quality, and the Irish know how to cook.'

The Abbess looked slightly mollified.

81   F

'They are the oldest Christian civilisation in Europe,' continued the Archbishop. 'It is true that the best of their writers and artists are, or were, Protestants, and came over to England to work, but, nevertheless, there is an atmosphere of culture in Ireland far more obviously than in England, though I admit that at times ecclesiastical pressure is a trifle severe.'

The Abbess, pondering, said nothing.

'A coach has been reserved for you on the boat train from Euston tomorrow night,' continued the Archbishop.

'The boat train? What boat?' cried the Abbess. '*Another* crossing of the ocean! My nuns could not stand it. Are we to be separated by two oceans from France? But it is really the Finisterre, this *Irelande* ! '

'It is half-way to America.'

'*Quelle horreur* ! I wish to be on the doorstep of Europe, no farther.'

'Well, there it is. You won't be on a fishing boat, but on a big comfortable ship.'

'But how shall we live? With what money? Do they use money in Ireland . . . or cowrie shells . . . ?'

'You can let the fishing rights on the two lakes, for large sums of money. You can charge a shilling to see the arboretum. You own a summer hotel on the seashore. You own farms and other properties including two villages. The mansion is large enough for you to take in paying guests, as you did at Soissons. There is no food rationing in Ireland.'

The Abbess's face lit up. If there was money to be made, that was not so bad. Her frugal and acquisitive French mind was already calculating what their income would be.

She turned to the Archbishop. '*Eh bien, Monseigneur, vous êtes un ange* to take all this trouble. We will pray for you every day, and you must pray for us, poor exiles, speaking only French—by the way, what language do they speak in Ireland?'

'English. Though they have a strange uncouth language of their own, they seldom use it. Certainly I will remember you every day at Mass.' The Archbishop led her gently to the door. She knelt to receive his final benediction, rose and bowed to the Bishop, then, followed by a scurrying shadow clutching a notebook to its bosom, she retired.

The Archbishop heaved a sigh of relief and finished the bottle of wine. Primly, the Bishop poured himself out another cup of tea. Both prelates looked satisfied.

12

THEY HAD a smooth crossing. As the ship moved quietly on through the still night, the Abbess got out of bed and looked out of the porthole. There was only the path of moonlight over a calm and empty sea. The Abbess experienced once again the sensation of being suspended between two worlds, two phases of existence. She felt also a chilling sensation in her bones that she was old and would be allowed to fight no more. That this château in Ireland, suitable though it might be in every way for the Community, was, in truth, exile, banishment. It was to keep her out of mischief that they had been sent to Ireland. She knelt down by the side of the bunk and prayed for a long time. 'O God, help me to bear the onset of old age, and take me soon unto yourself.'

She found her nuns in rather better spirits the next morning than they had been on arrival at Southampton, for they had had a comfortable passage. They all came up on deck early and sat about in the dawn saying their office and gazing out over the beauty of Dublin bay and the Wicklow mountains behind.

At North Wall they found that a four-hour train journey lay before them. The train passed at first through lush meadows full of grazing cows, and their spirits rose . . . this was perhaps not too uncivilised a country after all . . . moreover, they were given an excellent breakfast in the restaurant car. But then, after Athenry, the train began to crawl along, across miles of desolate bog, and their spirits fell. Finally they arrived at Galway. Here they were met by an ebullient, elderly woman, who declared herself to be a sculptor and a Catholic convert and a cousin of the Prime Minister. This lady, with some helpers, provided them with cups of tea, and were very kind, though the Abbess did not believe their pretensions. Why would a cousin of the great Churchill live in this outlandish place?

'Is that our château?' inquired the Abbess pointing to the buildings of Galway University, and received a shock when informed that they had a drive of fifty miles before them in a bus.

'But why could we not continue by the train?' inquired the Abbess, and was horrified to discover that Lingmoor Abbey was situated fifty miles from a railway station.

They got into the bus. It was a fine bus, with chairs that stayed upright or lolled back at the press of a button, with a sunshine roof, a lavatory, and a stewardess. It rolled away across a landscape of small fields with rocks in them, to Cong, and then along the sad shores of Lough Corrib. On the left, in the distance, rose the Seven Pins of Connemara, a dark blue line along the horizon; on the right they caught occasional fjord-like glimpses of the sea. There were few houses or villages and no towns. They went on and on and the dusk began to gather. The Abbess and her nuns shivered. Where were they being taken? Never had they any of them been in a wilderness of such terrible abandonment.

Some of the nuns began to weep, from exhaustion and fear of the unknown. One and all would rather have been under heavy shell-fire at the front in a country familiar to them. The Abbess tried to comfort them. '*Allons, mes enfants, on va bientôt arriver*' . . . but she was near tears herself.

At long last, just as it got dark, the stewardess pointed out a large building some way off on the right. It was a blaze of light from attic to basement. Little figures could be seen gathered outside the main entrance which was wide open.

'See,' said the stewardess, 'they have prepared a welcome for you.'

As the bus turned into the drive, the true proportions of the vast mansion could be seen, in its setting of splendid trees, their tops outlined against the night sky, and the lake reflecting the lights from the house.

The Abbess was conscious of a sudden surge of pride. It was a fine dwelling, finer, though she did not yet admit it, than the convent at Soissons. She composed herself and prepared to make a dignified entry into her new home. As the bus drew up at the front door, she saw that there was indeed a crowd of about two hundred people gathered there. She descended first from the bus, stately, gracious, though she had cramp in her left leg, a smile on her handsome old face, her hand outstretched for those to kiss who felt so inclined, which few did, as Mitred Abbesses were unknown in Ireland. Still, there was no mistaking the warmth of their welcome. An amiable priest, who announced himself as their chaplain, escorted them into the house. The Abbess demanded to be taken first of all to the chapel, and when her nuns had all followed her in, they sang, in the lovely Benedictine chant, a Te Deum of thanksgiving for their safe arrival in their new home.

Then the chaplain escorted them to the diningroom where supper awaited them, and as she entered the room, the Abbess gave a shout of incredulous joy, for there, all round the walls, were the portraits of her ten predecessors, with the mitre, cope and crosier, which were in her luggage at this minute.

'*Mais comment est-il possible!*' she exclaimed, and

the priest explained that the Archbishop had arranged with the authorities in Paris where she had stored them just before the outbreak of war, to have them transported to Ireland in time to greet her on her arrival.

'*Ce bon prêtre!*' she said, as she walked slowly round the room. Yes, there they all were, Abbess Anne, Abbess Zoë, Abbess Clémentine, Abbess Dieudonnée, Abbess Clare, Abbess Marie-Jeanne, Abbess Jeanne, Abbess Alexandrine, Abbess Elizabeth, Abbess Léonie, and herself. Who would be the twelfth?

The next day she inspected her property: the house from top to bottom in the morning, the outdoors in the afternoon. She expressed herself well satisfied with all she saw, and only wished the whole thing could be transported bodily to France.

'There is one rather unfortunate fact of which I must inform you, Madame,' said the agent, who was showing her round. 'The property is not insured against fire or theft, the reason being that it is so far away from the nearest police station (ten miles), or fire station (fifty miles . . . Galway or Westport), that it is impossible for either of these bodies to reach you in time in the event of an emergency.'

'*Ça n'a pas d'importance,*' declared the Abbess loftily, and later unpacked the statue of Our Lady which she carried everywhere with her, and taking it to the chapel, she installed it on the Altar of Our

Lady. Then looking at it severely she wagged an admonitory finger. '*C'est à vous, Madame,*' she said. '*Vous serez notre assurance, hein?*' And turning, she stalked out of the chapel.

13

THE WAR was now over; it had ended, to her deep disgust, with the Abbess taking no part in the liberation of her country. She was old and forgotten now. Then the Abbess heard one day on her radio that Pétain was going to be tried at Riom. She fell into one of her rare rages, but luckily there was no one else in the room. 'How *dare* they! How *dare* they!' she kept repeating, and as soon as she heard the date of the trial, she turned the offending instrument off, and went to the chapel to pray.

But what was it doing, this Fourth Republic! Pétain, the hero of Verdun, on trial for his life! Pushed into a position of supreme responsibility at the age of 90, with the Germans already installed in the country, what could he do but 'collaborate' and try to get the best terms possible for his unhappy people? The Abbess was too well aware of the subtle encroachments of old age upon the intellect not to know what difficulties Pétain must have undergone. If she found it hard to rule her convent at 70, with no Germans to order her about, what must it have been like for an old man of 90 to try and rule a country under the noses of the conquerors? She was not long making up her mind. She would go to Riom and give evidence at the trial.

She sat down at her writing desk and wrote a letter to the lawyer defending the Marshal, whose name had been announced on the radio. She told him of her connection with Pétain, and asked to be allowed to testify on his behalf.

A week later she received a very nice letter from the lawyer, full of admiration at her decision to make the long journey from Ireland in order to testify for the Marshal, but ending his letter, 'We all know about the hero of Verdun, Madame, but, alas, the man who saved France's honour at Verdun, lost it at Montoire.'

The Abbess went to Riom, nevertheless. Her appearance in the court-room caused a sensation. Many people present had thought she was dead. She, too, had been a great heroine in her day. Now, the fire of those days had departed, she moved stiffly but still with dignity, she had grown very stout, but her voice was as warm and rich and full of sympathy as ever. Pétain leaned forward in the dock and cupped his ear in his hand the better to hear what she said. She was shocked at his appearance. She had not seen him for more than twenty years. Her rage welled up within her. How could they put this poor old dotard on trial for his life, he who had once deserved so well of his country! It was plain that he was not fully aware of what he was doing.

'I call Madame de Soissons,' said Pétain's counsel.

In the witness box the Abbess related in a low, clear voice what she had known of the actions of General Pétain at Verdun and how he had saved France, of how she knew him to be a good practising Catholic and a good patriot.

When she had finished speaking a wave of futility engulfed her. She had done no good. The Procureur de la République indicated that he would not question her. The senior judge, leaning forward, said to her, 'We all admire your courage and determination in travelling all the way from your new and distant home to come here. Madame de Soissons needs no eulogies from me. She has long been a national heroine. But I am bound to say that the brave hero of Verdun is not the same man as the cowardly Marshal of Montoire.'

The Abbess's rage burst out. 'Have you no sense of honour,' she cried, 'of dignity, of decency! Putting Field Marshal Pétain in the dock with *canaille* like Laval!' She pointed a scornful finger at Laval, who winced and reddened. 'I see,' she went on, 'that in this shabby Fourth Republic, there is no place for those who love the honour of France and our holy religion.' She opened her cloak and showed the two medals on her breast. She unpinned them. 'These were given me,' she said, 'for helping to save the honour of France. But now there is no honour. I am glad I live far off in Ireland. I can no longer wear the battle honours of a country which is dying of shame.' And walking over to Pétain, she gently put the medals in his hands, closed the hands over them and kissed them. '*Vous me les avez donné, Monsieur le Maréchal, je vous les rends.*'

Then turning, she bowed to Madame Pétain, bowed more deeply to the judges, and stumped out of the court-room. The whole assembly was in tears.

Rising, the Procureur Général, who was due to sum up, made his speech. The death penalty had been fully expected. But he wound up with: 'I intended to ask for the death penalty, but Madame de Soissons has recalled to our minds what this poor old man once was, and what, *hélas*, we are today . . . I don't deny it. I therefore ask for *réclusion perpétuelle*.'

So Pétain was sentenced to perpetual banishment on the Ile de Ré, and when he died, a few years later, Madame Pétain put the Abbess's two medals between his fingers, entwined in the rosary, and they were buried with him in the grave.

14

THE DAY of the Abbess Catherine's Jubilee was approaching. Fifty years an Abbess! In some ways it seemed so long; in others so short. So short in that the daily rhythm of prayer and work and the chanting of the Divine Office in choir continued day after day and the days merged quickly into one another, and so the years flew by . . . long, in that this rhythm had been punctuated with interruptions, with wars and fights and journeys, ending in exile, which made the time seem to have been long indeed.

Great preparations were being made locally to celebrate the Abbess's Jubilee. She was supposed to know nothing about them, they were to be a great surprise, but of course she knew everything. She always did. It made her sad, and she felt guilty because here were all these people striving and organising to make her Jubilee day a success, and she still could not love them.

No . . . after ten years among them, she could not love the Irish. It was no good. She had tried. She prayed for them and to be granted the grace to love them, but she continued to have an ineradicable antipathy towards them, their sad-looking country, their weeping climate, their remoteness, their curious, happy-go-lucky religion, which was so weak on rubrics and ritual and ignored everything the Pope said.

And then, really in some ways they were so impossibly childish that it was hard to be patient with them. No sense of logic at all, and the most absurd ideas. (The Abbess had never heard of the Blarney Stone!) For instance, her chaplain, Father O'Mahoney, professed to believe in 'the Little People'.

'Not to be confused with fairies,' he said. 'Fairies are immortal spirits, maybe good, or maybe evil, but the Little People are mortal. They are the residue of the original Irish, who were driven farther and farther west by Danish and Anglo-Saxon invaders, and had to take refuge in underground forts, which have degenerated into what tourists call "fairy mounds". They are related to the beehive hut, of course.'

'Then why, if these creatures are mortal,' said the Abbess, 'do you not preach the Gospel to them, as is your bounden duty? Do you mean to tell me that for two thousand years you have allowed this pagan race to live side by side with you and done nothing about it?'

'They are incurably pagan,' said the chaplain.

'Contumacious, or invincibly ignorant . . . incapable by nature of appreciating the Gospel . . . I don't know.'

'But that is nonsense. If they are mortal, they are men, and Christ died for all men as you very well know.'

'But how can we get at them? They live underground.'

'Smoke them out. And when they come out, turn them across your knee and spank them! That is what I would do!'

'Why don't you then? There are plenty of them on the property.'

'Nonsense. I don't believe it.'

'Why, one of your own nuns, Sister Brigit O'Shaugnessy, puts out a bottle of milk for them every night, and it is always gone in the morning.'

'I know she does. I told her she ought to go to Confession for aiding and abetting such pagan customs, but as you are her confessor, it would not do much good. Of course the bottle of milk is gone in the morning. Some tramp takes it, or perhaps Brigit herself comes out and goes behind a tree and drinks it.'

'Oh, no, Brigit wouldn't do that. She is a very honest girl. Why, your protégée, Eileen O'Mara, whom you told me you hoped would become Abbess one day, is a great friend of the Little People. She sees them scampering about all over the place near her home. Now I'll tell you something, Abbess. I was fishing one of the loughs near Clifden one time, and I was sitting on a little mound, and my rod lay on the ground beside me and to it I had just attached a new fly, and I was filling my pipe. When out from under the mound comes one of the Little People, dressed in green doublet and hose as in the Middle Ages (for they have no opportunity to see fashion displays any more than you nuns have, and they dress in the same period), and whips the fly off my line, sticks it in his hat, gives a shrill laugh, and is off into his burrow before I can catch him.'

'I don't believe a word of it,' said the Abbess, 'and if it is true, I am all the more glad to be leaving Ireland.'

'I have heard there are Little People in Brittany.'

'There may be. I am not going to Brittany, which is almost as uncivilised as Ireland.'

'But what is this about your leaving Ireland, Abbess?'

'*Ah, mon dieu*, I did not mean to mention it so soon. Keep it, I beg you . . . how you say . . . under your hat. I shall announce it at the banquet that is so kindly being given for me.'

At the banquet, the Abbess felt most uncomfortable. The whole neighbourhood, including all the notables, the chief of police, the doctor, the lawyer, all the leading farmers, were present. Everyone had brought a gift. A firework display had been arranged on the lawn. The boats on the lake were decorated with Chinese lanterns. They drank her health repeatedly and sang 'for she's a jolly good fellow'. There was no mistaking their warmth and affectionate sympathy. But the Abbess rose to make her speech with a feeling of guilt. Never before in her life had she said anything insincere. Yet now . . . how could she tell these people that she did not love them, that she still felt, after ten years in their midst, a most unchristian dislike of them, their climate, their customs, their superstitions, everything about them, and that it would be quite intolerable to her to have to spend the rest of her days among them? Instead, she had to say how happy she was to be among them, what a wonderful day her Jubilee had been (and in a way it had . . . telegrams of congratulation pouring in from all over France, a case of champagne from the Archbishop of Rheims, an Apostolic Blessing from the Pope, conveyed personally by the Nuncio in Dublin), and yet, something lacking, the mutual love and sympathy which should have been there. It was in tears, not of happiness but of frustration, that she ended her speech with the words, 'And now I intend to abdicate, and return to France to spend my last days in my own country.'

A groan of consternation passed round the table, followed by cries of protest, but the Abbess, bowing to the company, had risen from her seat and left the room. For the next few hours she was on her knees in the chapel, her face hidden in her hands and the tears streaming down her cheeks.

15

'Fire! Fire!' The young Abbess Eileen heard the words shouted in a man's voice through her sleep, and still half asleep smelt smoke in her nostrils, and when she finally woke up properly, the far end of her room was obscured by smoke.

She jumped out of bed, wrapped her big black cloak round her, seized her pectoral cross and ring and put them on, so that in the panic everyone, guests and boarders as well as nuns, would know who she was. Then, pinning on her veil as she ran from the room, she made for the chapel. One of the nuns was already there and had removed the Blessed Sacrament. Father O'Mahoney soon appeared in his dressing-gown and took It from her. The nun then ran to the sacristy and removed the cope and mitre and crosier, the monstrances and reliquaries, while the Abbess removed the more valuable of the vestments.

She then ran to her office and dialled the fire brigades of Cong, Clifden, Galway and Westport, but they were all a long way off, the volunteer crews had to be summoned, and get up and get dressed, and it was obvious that none would arrive before the fire had got a good hold.

The young Abbess next ran to the head of the main staircase, in the part of the house reserved for guests and boarders. She could now see flames coming from downstairs, where the panelling of the dining-room and drawing-room were fiercely burning.

Two of the American fishermen had taken down the portraits of the twelve Abbesses and had stacked them on the lawn; when, later, Abbess Eileen discovered this, she duly thanked them but was secretly rather annoyed that they had been spared, and then annoyed with herself for being annoyed. But in her heart she had always thoroughly disapproved of the French connection, and one of her aims was to make the Community thoroughly Irish. She had an idea that all the French were immoral, except of course the religious, but even they were too worldly for her liking, and her intense admiration for Madame Catherine did not alter her opinion of Frenchwomen in general. Madame Catherine, indeed, had frequently shocked her. Dame Eileen had looked forward to the day when she could separate from the French Congregation and become simply the Irish Benedictines of Lingmoor Abbey with herself as the Lady Abbess, no more. And now Lingmoor Abbey was fiercely burning. She remembered that among her reforms was one which had flashed into her mind once and out again and been put aside for the moment as a minor matter, and that was fire drill. Now she realised how foolish she had been. She saw that the guests, grappling on the lawn with the hoses, had no idea how they worked and were having little more success with the foam ejectors, and that, in any case, the hoses fell short in length of the lake by some four yards.

Meanwhile the Abbess counted her nuns. They were all there. The part of the house where they slept, at the back, faced on to the cliff against which the house was built. By opening their windows, they could jump down on to the cliff-face, and work their way round to the front of the house, which they had all succeeded in doing. The novice mistress, who had kept her head, had passed them all out this way, and they stood in sad groups on the lawn wrapped in blankets and their shifts among the guests and boarders in pyjamas and nightgowns. The Abbess alone was dressed.

She stood there and watched her beloved Lingmoor burn, and with it were consumed her hopes. Her brain was slowly numbing with the horror of it all. As the full measure of the catastrophe began to dawn on her, seeing the roof cave in, and watching the pitiful attempts of the helpers to fetch water from the lake, she found herself praying, 'O God, why did You do this to me?'

It was three years before she found out why.

16

THERE WAS one obvious thing to do: move to the
hotel which the Abbey owned four miles away on
the seashore. Luckily the season was over and there
were no guests. The building was in fact closed for
redecoration. The Abbess and her nuns moved in.
The ballroom became the chapel. It was in many
ways inconvenient. The nuns had not got rooms to
themselves, and did not always care for sharing,
complaining all the time of little things, such as that
their stable companions snored. The French nuns
were the worst grumblers. They thought it *triste*
and *morne* when the Atlantic rollers came thundering
in beneath a grey sky of swiftly driven clouds, and
the gale roared and the fuchsia and hydrangea
hedges were bent to the ground, and the rain came
lashing down.

On one fine morning, with the wind only a whisper and a pale sun, the Abbess put on her cope and
mitre and carrying her heavy silver crosier, placed
herself, as ordered by the rubrics in the event of a
calamity, at the head of the Community, and they
walked down the drive and round the village and

back again, the high clear voice of the young Abbess intoning the penitential psalms, and the confused murmur of the nuns behind her, as they repeated her words, falling on the ears of a few fisher-folk, who knelt in the roadway as the procession passed by.

'And now,' said the young Abbess to herself, as she took off the heavy cope in the sacristy, 'we must begin again at the beginning.'

17

MADAME EILEEN never liked Kellerman Hall, as the hotel was called. Nor did her nuns, and a community of discontented females, even though religiously inclined, is a fearsome thing to contend with. The young Abbess quailed at the task before her, at the same time as she sympathised. They missed the feeling of cosiness and security at Lingmoor, the huge trees, the placid waters of the lakes, the sheltering hillside behind. The open Atlantic was only palatable on a few days of the year. Moreover, they did not get the visitors nor make the money as they used to do. No trout or salmon fishing, no sheltered walks in bad weather. Golden sands and fuchsia hedges, but not as delectable as elsewhere. The Americans, while liking to come to Connemara to fish, and prepared to pay for it, preferred the Mediterranean, or their own California, to bathe in. Dame Eileen, indeed, never regarded Kellerman Hall as anything but a temporary home. She would have liked to rebuild Lingmoor, but the cost was prohibitive. A fund had been started, sponsored by the Cardinal-Primate, but the response had hitherto been meagre. It seemed as if the Irish were unconcerned as to whether their own Benedictine Abbey of women should remain in the island or not.

'We must pray for guidance,' the Abbess told her nuns. 'We must make a novena. I cannot believe it is God's will that we should remain here, quarrelling and restless. We must pray hard to know His will and where we are to go.'

For three years they prayed before His will was revealed to them, and then, as is so often the case, it was not at first acceptable, and they scarcely believed it. His instrument was a Miss Nesta Myers.

Miss Myers was a gaunt, mysterious Englishwoman of uncertain age and considerable intelligence and drive, who booked rooms for three weeks in the late spring of 1958. She and the Abbess took to one another at once. Miss Myers's downright manner appealed to Dame Eileen, perhaps as a contrast to her own rather oblique approach to problems.

One day they went to look at the ruins of Lingmoor. Even in its bleak and blackened state, the interior gaping open to the sky, it looked to Dame Eileen a fine and noble building in its superb setting of lakes, woods, and gorse-covered hills.

'If only we could get it back!' she said to her companion.

'Nonsense!' said Miss Myers. 'That is not your destiny. That is not what God wants of you.'

'What does He want then?' replied the Abbess with her gentle smile. 'I only wish I knew.'

'It's obvious,' answered Miss Myers. 'The destiny, fortune and prosperity of this Community has always lain in France. Every excursion elsewhere has always been disastrous, both spiritually and materially. For two hundred and fifty years you have been Les Dames de Soissons, and written a long and glorious chapter in both French and Benedictine history. Your predecessors, whose portraits you can see in the ballroom at Kellerman Hall, were all French, all the Mitred Abbesses except yourself. You, my dear, are Madame de Soissons in exile, and no one else.'

'Never! Never!' cried the Abbess indignantly. 'I will never go back to France. I wish to sever the French connection as soon as possible and become totally Irish.'

'Maybe, but does God want you to?'

'Why not? God has nothing against the Irish. On the contrary.'

'Nor against the French so far as I am aware. It is you who are prejudiced against the "Eldest Daughter of the Church", not God.'

'But what would I do in France, Nesta? Some of

107

the older nuns would be pleased, yes. But I am determined to make an Irish Community.'

'And where will you live?'

'Not at Kellerman Hall,' said the Abbess. 'I don't yet know where. What would we do in France? I don't know a word of French.'

'Teach English to girls of good family. Take in boarders as your predecessors did. Become fashionable.'

Dame Eileen laughed. 'Can you see me, the girl from the claddagh, becoming fashionable, the girl who never went to school, teaching English!'

'A Mitred Abbess, even if she were deaf and dumb, would always be an attraction to a certain type of smart Parisian, and if in addition she is Irish, and very pretty, charming everyone with that soft Irish accent . . .'

'Oh, shut up!' laughed the Abbess. 'You are being quite absurd.'

'Not at all. I repeat, the destiny of your House is in France. I, and other teachers whom I can easily find, will do the teaching and the smartening up, and the nuns will give moral tone and spiritual instruction. I am going over to Paris when my stay here comes to an end to fix things up for you provisionally, find you a house and so on. Yours is a glorious future, my dear.'

'Never! never! never!' cried the Abbess.

'I seem to remember hearing (or did you tell me

yourself?) how you once used those same words, equally emphatically, and had to retract them later. Did you not, when Madame Catherine told you she had selected you for Abbess, assure her that never, never, never, would you accept?'

'Yes,' confessed the Abbess.

'Yet you did accept. And are you sorry?'

'It is a great responsibility being Abbess.'

'If you were suddenly relegated to the ranks by Rome and someone else made Abbess in your place, would you be glad?'

'I should accept it.'

'Of course you would,' said Miss Myers impatiently, 'in a spirit of obedience and humility and all that. But you wouldn't like it. You like being Abbess because of the power it gives you. No, don't deny it! Everyone likes power. Some, like yourself, use it worthily to good ends. But you wouldn't like to have to hand over your reforming ideas to somebody else!'

'You probe too deep, Nesta. You're worse than my Confessor!' laughed the Abbess.

'You could not imagine at one time being Abbess. Now you cannot imagine yourself as an Abbess in France. But you will be. God wants you to be. I want you to be. Madame Catherine wants you to be. Three very stalwart antagonists, you see!'

The Abbess laughed. 'If I were allowed to bet and

I had any money, I'd bet you a shilling that we'll never go back to France.'

'Done, my dear,' said Miss Myers, 'but make it 50 francs.'

18

FOR SOME time Dame Eileen struggled on at Kellerman Hall, but at last began to lose heart. She, the great reforming Abbess, and she couldn't even keep the Community as they were, much less reform them! They were sliding backwards, growing daily more cantankerous, more irritable, less prayerful, less homogeneous. Feuds, bickerings, cliques, jealousies, perpetual lamentations from the French nuns, who still formed nearly half the Community, continual sneers at Ireland, and the climate, countered by ripostes about the immorality of the French, were the order of the day. Not a sign from Miss Myers. The last summer visitor departed. The beach was swept by equinoctial gales, bringing torrents of rain. The nuns, having finished their *Orare*, were unable to *Laborare*, for it was impossible to go outside, though the French nuns were more adept at needlework, cooking and *astiquer*-ing the parquet floor of the ballroom (now the chapel), until it was so slippery that they skated over it on their way to say their prayers. The peat fire in the recreation room blew back down the chimney and covered them all in smoke. The road out to the point was under water and the tradesmen's vans could not get through. The nuns began to run short of food.

Finally the young Abbess summoned three of the hardiest young nuns and together the four of them, hooded and cloaked, with baskets on their arms, set forth to the general store at Lingmoor village, as the shops in the opposite direction along the sea road, though nearer, were cut off. Their way took them through the grounds of Lingmoor Abbey, and as soon as they reached the shelter of the arboretum, down the long grass rides, the wind died away to a distant riffling in the tree-tops and the rain lessened to a gentle drizzle. When they reached the ruined Abbey and the lakes, the water was placid, for the high hill at the back of the house protected it from the gale.

The Abbess felt suddenly rebellious. Why had God permitted this beautiful place to be burnt? Why this unreasonable cross to bear when here she might have done great things! But she knew that she had been given four years in which to practise fire drill and had never done so. 'My fault,' she moaned to herself . . . '*mea maxima culpa.*' There was the rock on which she had sat and thought great things . . . and thought with pride of the line of her predecessors, the Ladies of Soissons . . . with pride, then, of their French connection. Could it be God's will after all that they should return to France? For indeed

Ireland had not accepted them as she had expected it would. Nearly all their visitors were English, American, German, French. The Irish practically ignored them, except the local inhabitants. She had engaged a well-known priest to give retreats, but no one had applied. Vocations were slow in coming in.

But if it were God's will that they should return to France, what about their *dea ex machina*, Miss Myers, without whose help Dame Eileen could make no move? She seemed to have forgotten them.

But she had not. After enduring a long, wet, windy winter, during which the Community became more and more surly, one balmy spring day came a telegram: 'Arriving tonight with great news, Nesta.'

She duly appeared, and after first kneeling to and then embracing the Abbess, she proclaimed, 'Marvellous news for you, my dear. It has taken a long time, and I did not want to buoy you up with false hopes, so did not get in touch with you till I was quite sure . . . which I am now. I have found you a beautiful Abbey, a lovely old château with a seventeenth-century gem of a chapel, lovely grounds, a lake, flower and vegetable and herb gardens. I have found a competent staff, and it is in the fashionable Valley of the Chevreuse, just outside Paris, at Auray-sur-Seine; you will be known as the Ladies of Auray, and the Métro is close by, but it is quite country and very beautiful, best Île de France landscape, so civilised, and you will love it. And of course your old Abbess Catherine whom I went to see in Paris is delighted you are coming back and will often come and see you—and Auray is very fashionable and full of famous Anglophils who want their children to learn English.'

Miss Myers stopped for breath. The young Abbess sat silent in a daze, trying vainly to digest this spate of information following so swiftly on so long a silence. Finally she rang her bell. 'Bring me some tea,' she said. 'Hot, strong, and sweet!' and to Nesţa, 'If I don't have some, I shall faint!'

19

In May the Abbess went to Paris to inspect what might become her property, and possibly negotiate for its purchase. She took one of the French nuns with her and was accompanied also by Miss Myers.

She had never before left Ireland and her self-consciousness made her even more stiff and reserved than usual. Many travellers at Victoria and Dover wondered who the tall, beautiful young woman wearing the large gold crucifix and chain and the ruby ring could be. On the Liverpool boat and as far as Euston the Irish stared, and seemed uncertain whether to bow or genuflect or take no notice. The Abbess, throughout the journey, stared straight in front of her with unseeing eyes.

The Channel crossing to Calais was very rough. The Abbess tried hard to preserve her dignity as she felt, for the first time, the pangs of seasickness. She tried to say her office but found it hard to concentrate. She gazed out of the window of the saloon at what seemed to her mountainous seas, and shuddered. She noticed that the people round her were all busy talking, apparently quite unconcerned, so she stopped saying terrified Hail Marys under her breath, and drew herself up, determined to be both dignified and courageous . . . Her companion was already green and prostrate. Miss Myers was happily pacing the deck and enjoying the spectacle of the heavy seas. But at last the Abbess's beringed hand reached out for the china bowl, and she gave in wholly and completely, dignity thrown to the wind.

How good it was to climb into the warm train at Calais, and hear the hiss of the steam in the pipes and watch the gendarmes, through the writhing mist wraiths, pacing up and down the platform, and then to be able to say one's office in peace. And when the train had started and rumbled away through the ruined town on to the uplands leading to Boulogne, a smart attendant with *Voiture Ambulant* on his cap appeared, with a trayful of delicious buttery croissants, sandwiches, and cups of steaming coffee. The Abbess began to feel better.

Miss Myers pointed out the basilica of the Sacré Cœur against the darkening sky, white and gleaming, as they entered the cavern of the Gare du Nord; she soon piloted them to a taxi which sped them across Paris till suddenly they saw on the left the floodlit façade of Notre-Dame, with the light shining also from inside to illuminate the rose window, and the Abbess gave thanks to God and His Mother for allowing her to see such a thing.

At length they reached the dark little respectable

116

hotel on the Left Bank where they were to spend the night. It was near the Rue du Bac, and so, after a meal at which the Abbess for the first time in her life drank wine, and found that she liked it, they walked out to that universal place of pilgrimage of which Our Lady is perpetual Prioress, and where you still may see the chair on which She sat.

Next morning after Mass they took the Métro for the Valley of the Chevreuse. Suburban at first, it grew quite countrified, with that very special beauty of the Île de France in the spring, more delicate and tender than the thicker colours of Ireland, so gracious with its water-meadows and poplars, its woods and low hills, so civilised with its charming houses half hidden in the trees, that the young Abbess could not help saying to herself, 'I would not mind living here.'

She had been less than twenty-four hours in France, but already she was beginning to feel something of the *douceur de vivre* which takes the heart of all foreigners, and to compare it not unfavourably with the sadness and savagery of her native land.

After leaving the Métro they had a walk of half an hour till they reached some wrought-iron gates supported by stone posts at the entrance to a shady drive leading up to a big old château on a slight rise.

The Abbess was attracted to it at once. It was like a more gracious and sophisticated Lingmoor. The caretaker and his wife met them, genuflected and kissed the Abbess's ring. The interior of the house seemed suitable in every way, but when the Abbess saw the chapel she let out a gasp. The caretaker turned on all the lights and she gasped again, for it was utterly unlike anything she had ever seen or imagined, and at first she had difficulty in believing that it was a chapel at all.

The style was the very wildest and most extravagant rococo, by an Austrian architect, a riot of cherubs and saints and angels hanging and swinging in every conceivable position from a blue and gold ceiling and clinging to twisted pillars, themselves wreathed in golden vines and silver ivy. On one side there was a feature resembling a stage box, high up, overlooking the High Altar, with sky-blue velvet curtains and pelmets, which had been the family pew. 'Your pew, Madame,' said the caretaker, pointing to it proudly.

'Oh, never!' cried the startled Abbess, adding, 'The Cardinal will never consecrate this!'

Miss Myers laughed. 'It is consecrated,' she said, 'and he will come to your inauguration. Old Madame de Soissons, old Madame Catherine told him to, and no one disobeys her! Besides His Eminence likes rococo.'

'Is that what it is called?'

'Yes, and it was invented by the Jesuits, who thought it would bring the eighteenth century to church . . . which it did.'

'Well, the Continentals have strange taste, I must say. Do you like it, Nesta?'

'Yes. I think it's great fun . . . You are a funny little Puritan, Eileen, like all the Irish. Victorian Gothic and beehive huts . . . that's about their limit of taste! You will get used to this in time. Now for some luncheon. There's a little pub in the village where they give you quite a good meal. At three the family lawyer is coming to answer any questions you may wish to put to him, and to discuss terms of sale. You can raise a loan on your future prospects.'

'Lunch in a pub?' said the Abbess. 'Is that quite the thing?'

'Certainly, and we have a guest whom you will be glad to meet.'

As they turned into the garden of the little hotel, there, sitting in a basket chair in the May sunshine, was the old Abbess.

20

THE OLD LADY embraced the young Abbess with warm affection.

'I knew you would come,' she said, 'as soon as dear Miss Myers came to see me and asked me to pray for you. How wonderful to have you settled at last in our dear France!'

'I haven't decided anything yet, *ma mère*,' said the young Abbess.

'But you have seen,' said Madame Catherine in surprise, as if to see France produced instant conversion. Like all French people she could not believe that once you had seen France and smelt its delicious mixture of drains, coffee and garlic, you could do otherwise than fall in love with it and immediately want to live there. It was like any other conversion. First you lived in invincible ignorance, but as soon as, by God's grace, you were brought in contact with the truth (namely, that France is the only civilised country in the world), you were glad to submit. The old Abbess believed that all the earth before the Fall must have resembled France, which was all that was left of the Earthly Paradise.

'After all,' murmured the young Abbess, half to herself, 'it doesn't really matter much where one lives. One is with God, and one lives with Him.'

'How much better to live with Him in Paradise than in purgatory,' said Madame Catherine.

'I would not call Ireland purgatory, *ma mère*,' said Dame Eileen, 'though I admit that the conditions in which we have recently been living there resemble it.'

'And do you mean to go on living in those conditions for the rest of your life?' asked Miss Myers. 'For I fail to see what is to change them, unless you sell your property at Lingmoor, including Kellerman Hall, set up here, and buy the château, on the proceeds.'

'I must go and pray,' said the young Abbess. 'Is that the village church over there?'

'Yes. I will stay and keep Madame Catherine company.'

'Do not hurry,' said Madame Catherine. 'Pray long and hard and you will learn God's will.'

The Abbess was gone at least an hour. Madame Catherine put on her spectacles and tried to say her office but soon nodded and dozed in the sun. Miss Myers beside her was already fast asleep. The French nun had accompanied the young Abbess. It was all very quiet and beautiful on that lovely afternoon in May. After a time, the old Abbess's spectacles fell off and dangled from one ear, her legs were wide apart, her hands clasped on her stomach and there was a bee on her nose. At last the young Abbess came back. She hadn't the heart to wake the old lady, but though she carefully removed the bee from her nose, Madame Catherine must have been aware of it in her dreams, for, wheezing and grunting and sighing, she woke up.

'We will come here,' the young Abbess said rather wearily. 'I am sure it is God's will and the will of His Mother also. I listened in the stillness of that little church (which I like so much better than the castle chapel), and at last I knew. Yes, I see it now. Our destiny is here. In Ireland we were in exile from our real home, though not I, but the Community, and it is my job to serve the Community and do whatever is best for their welfare, and that is to return to France.'

'You will get a good price for Lingmoor,' said Madame Catherine, 'which will cover the expenses of your move here and the purchase of the château.'

'Aren't you going to say you are glad I have decided we shall come here?' asked the young Abbess reproachfully.

'But of course I am glad, *petite*,' answered the old Abbess, 'but being French I calculate the cost first always, practical you see, and anyway I have known for so long that you are coming, ever since I first began to pray for it a year ago.'

The young Abbess smiled ... 'What with you and God ...'

'*Il n'y a rien à faire*,' the Abbess Catherine finished the sentence for her, and then composed herself once more for sleep.

Envoi

THE STORY of the Ladies of Soissons, now the Ladies of Auray-sur-Seine, has however *not* been told. The outward adventures which befell them between 1688 and 1960, the ups and downs of fame and fate, the transplantings, the exiles, the wars, the revolutions, all these were simply interruptions to the real life of the Community, which is one of continuous prayer and work.

This story has, too, been told largely from the point of view of the Abbesses, and the sixty or so members of the Community have been anonymous as they would wish to be. They were simply women of prayer. Prayer, which is only talking to God, was their life blood, and still is, and over the centuries they have talked far more to God than to any human being. This is true even of the Abbesses. Even the most worldly, such as the Abbess Clare, the most ineffective such as the Abbess Zoë, the most luxurious such as the Abbess Anne, the most timid such as the Abbess Léonie, the most formidable, such as the Abbess Catherine, were all women of prayer, and, like their nuns, spent the greater part of their lives praying. Day after day, month after month, year after year, century after century, the Ladies of Soissons and Auray have prayed for about ten hours a day, the public prayer of the Church, sung to the beautiful Benedictine chant, special prayers ordered for the Community such as Novenas, Holy Mass each morning, and then the private prayer of each religious.

And if they were not praying or sleeping (and their sleep was interrupted every night when they rose to sing the night office), they would be fulfilling the other great Benedictine injunction: to work. They would be weeding or hoeing or planting or picking or digging or mending or washing or polishing or sewing or painting or hammering or cooking, or making vestments, or writing appeals, or haymaking, or milking cows.

What we have described in these pages are simply the accidents which from time to time interfered with this routine of *Orare et Laborare*, and rippled the calm surface of their lives.

For that is the object and *raison d'être* of a Benedictine's life, whether a monk or a nun, and the Community of the Ladies of Soissons could not have held together through all the vicissitudes we have described over the centuries if its life had not been based solidly on prayer and work. From the Community's viewpoint all that we have described, sometimes sad and sometimes gay, sometimes amusing, at other times tragic, often exciting, are trivia, annoying like a buzzing wasp, because interfering with routine: no more.

So we have not told their story, which is simply a long, indeed eternal, sometimes temporarily interrupted, talk with God. We have not told it because, by its very nature, it is a story which can never be told.